THE SCALE OF NATURE

Also by John Tyler Bonner

The Ideas of Biology
(Harper & Row)

Size and Cycle
(Princeton University Press)

The Cellular Slime Molds
(Princeton University Press)

The Evolution of Development
(Cambridge University Press)

Cells and Societies
(Princeton University Press and Atheneum)

Morphogenesis
(Princeton University Press and Atheneum)

THE SCALE

Illustrated by Patricia Collins

Harper & Row, Publishers

OF NATURE

by John Tyler Bonner

New York and Evanston

Contents

Preface   11

1.   *Introduction*   15

2.   *The Universe: Galaxies, Stars, and Planets*   30

3.   *The Crust*   48

4.   *A Community*   55

5.   *A Population*   66

6.   *An Organism*   80

7.   *Organs*   93

8.   *Tissues*   104

9.   *Cells*   117

10.   *Macromolecules*   127

11.   *Molecules*   137

12.   *Atoms*   146

13.   *Elementary Particles*   153

14.   *Conclusion*   158

Index   165

7

Illustrations

The Universe   17

A Galaxy   33

A Star   35

A Planet   37

The Earth's Crust   51

A Community   57

A Population   69

An Organism   83

An Organ   95

A Tissue   107

A Cell   119

Macromolecules   129

Molecules   139

An Atom   149

Elementary Particles   155

The Scale of Nature   159

9

Preface

THIS BOOK is written for someone who wishes to have a panoramic view of all of science. It will be considered very elementary by professionals in any one field of science, but that is my intention. I hope it will show how the various parts of science fit together, how they relate to one another. It may be helpful, also, to the student who wishes to decide what part of science would suit him best for a career.

I must confess that while the book was indeed written with all these high objectives in mind, there was another. It was to clarify my own mind and to see where my own area of special interest fits in with the rest of science. I have chosen to answer this question in as unsophisticated a way as possible, for it seemed to me in this instance that a simple answer would be as meaningful as a complex one. Furthermore, since the plan was to organize science on the basis of the size of objects, it seemed appropriate that the book should be, in part, a picture book, and it has been written with this specific aim in mind. As before, it has been a great pleasure working with Patricia Collins in putting ideas into pictures.

Since this book is a step in the process of my self-clarification, there is bound to be some curious unevenness in the emphasis. I am a biologist and not an astronomer, geologist, chemist, or physicist. Therefore the biology is at a slightly more advanced or detailed level than the other sciences. This is a deficiency on my part, which would not have been tolerated by a natural philosopher of the old school.

Besides the fact that the level of analysis is more elementary for the areas outside of biology, there was the great problem of whether or not they might also contain nonsense. I am most grateful to my friends Professors W. M. Elsasser and R. Sherr for saving me from such embarrassments and taking my education in hand. I am further indebted to Professor Elsasser for the title of the book. I must add thanks to Professor R. H. MacArthur and Mrs. Arthur Winfree for many helpful criticisms.

Finally, both Miss Collins and I would like to express our gratitude to Mr. Marshall Henrichs for his many helpful comments on problems of design of the book.

J.T.B.

Margaree Harbour
Cape Breton, Nova Scotia

THE SCALE OF NATURE

1

To PUT ALL OF SCIENCE IN ONE SLIM BOOK CAN only mean that the amount of material missing from these pages is almost without end. Our greatest difficulty today is that we have accumulated so much information about the worlds around us and each science has developed such specialized language, techniques, and even modes of thought, that the mere idea of putting it all together in a brief outline seems presumptuous, bordering upon the preposterous. Yet in doing so it is possible to obtain a perspective that is denied if one looks only at one science and not the others. Admittedly one learns very little science, but one learns something about science. One may compare the different approaches and see, at least to a superficial extent, what kinds of unknowns remain for each of the sciences.

The method to be used here to compare the various disciplines is a simple device. The objects of scientific study are classified on the basis of their size; this book will be a panoramic inquiry of large, middle-sized, and minute objects. With each size level there are

The Universe

THE series of plates in this book are a voyage from the very largest of objects to the very smallest. The plates begin with the unknown of the universe, which is shown here, and end with the unknown of the elementary particles within the atom, which is the last plate.

The two extremes in the size scale are invisible to us, and as we progress from either extreme to the middle of the size range, objects become progressively easier to see. Objects of intermediate size can be seen with the help of instruments such as microscopes and telescopes, while objects in our own size range can be seen with the naked eye.

It is estimated that there are roughly 10^{15} galaxies within the universe. The distance between galaxies lies in the order of millions to hundreds of millions of light years.

different approaches, different kinds of knowledge, and mainly different kinds of problems that need to be solved. Classification by size not only has the virtue of being a convenient and easy system, but also it reflects truly different categories of scientific endeavor.

The pursuit of science is a human undertaking entirely delineated by the mind of man. For this reason it is interesting that very large objects such as stars or very small objects such as atoms are too large or too small for us to be able to see or feel them directly, and this fact, in itself, sets them apart. Middle-sized objects such as animals and plants are within our experience and therefore, in some ways, we know more about them; for the most part they meet our expectations, our reason, our common sense. On the other hand, the science of very small or very large objects has often produced information that we could not have intuitively predicted from knowledge of ourselves. As examples one might cite the laws of gravity or the even more esoteric laws of relativity.

The fact that middle-sized objects are more familiar does not mean that they present fewer unsolved problems. Rather it is generally thought that some of the most important problems for the future involve living organisms, which lie in the middle size range. Again this is no doubt because of the basic interest in ourselves as living organisms, but there are other reasons also. One is that middle-sized living structures have a greater complexity in their internal construction than any other size level. Another is that no matter how many problems are solved, or facts discovered, there are always deeper ones that must be conquered. It is like trying to satisfy the greed of a miser; the more gold he gets, the more he desires. To some extent this is the reason science has become such a dominant force today in the intellectual life of our civilization, and again the reason for this, like the reason for the pursuit of science in the first place, lies in the peculiarities of our own psychological drives.

It is often said, especially by those who dispense money for research, that a particular area of science is the place to attack because it will provide the most exciting new information. But the historian of science tells us that this is mostly nonsense, for one cannot say where the important new discoveries will occur. Again there are many reasons for this uncertainty. Sometimes it depends upon whether or not the world is ready to receive the information. In some cases the advance bursts forth with instant acclaim, as was the case in the reception of Darwin's principle of natural selection. The world in fact was so ready that had Darwin not proclaimed it, Wallace and others would have made the notion popular at that receptive moment in our history. The fact that Darwin was a rare genius is an added pleasure but not an essential part of the progress of evolutionary thought in the last century. A classic example of an instance where the world was not ready for a brilliant discovery is that of Mendel's laws regarding heredity, which were published in 1866 but not appreciated until the early 1900's. Then they were received with eruptive acclaim; the world was ready. But the point here is that, in both these cases, prior to their widespread acceptance no one could have predicted that the next big breakthrough was to be in evolution or genetics. This is only obvious in retrospect. It is true that in technology the power of prediction is much greater, and we know from the experience of World War II that if money and scientific skill are poured into the right mold, all kinds of engineering advances will rapidly follow: radar, jet propulsion, and the control of nuclear energy. Such advances may even lead to the discovery of important new principles of science, but it is impossible to predict whether or not this will be so, or in what area of endeavor the new principles will appear.

Another important reason that the advance of science is unpredictable is that a major discovery almost invariably goes against the concepts and accepted views of the time. It is a major leap not just because of its own content, but also because of the difference between this content and the current dogma. Its shock value makes the truths seem not only self-evident but positively luminous in their boldness. This was true, for instance, of Copernicus' discovery of the sun being the center of our planetary system, Darwin's theory of natural selection, and Freud's hypotheses concerning the functioning of the mind. In each of these cases, there was violent controversy as the old and new ideas clashed, and the controversy did much to put the new theories in an especially high position in the minds of those who followed. The history of science is the history of the overcoming of prejudices and preconceptions. The advance is heralded by the foresight and genius of a few individuals, and the acceptance of the advance has to do with the more complex matter of the intellectual temper of the age.

I will indicate throughout this book where the active interest lies in each science, based upon present success and present dogmas. I cannot predict where the really significant advances will spring from—significant in the sense of being radically new departures from our current concepts. What predictions are made are on what new areas of science, although established, are still relatively untrammeled. Our predictions are reliable only when they apply to the clarification of areas in which the basic principles are already known. But it is impossible for us mortals to know when and where new principles will appear. They descend, like lightning from heaven, unexpected, disturbing, often destructive, but with a great flash of illumination.

Before we begin this sweeping survey of large, middle-sized, and small objects we must say something of the method of science. This is a much mistreated subject, and a few general words may not be amiss here. I have already stressed the extent to which science is a product of the human mind; it is therefore appropriate to discuss some of the modes of thought that comprise science.

It is often said that science is common sense. To some degree this is correct, although this quality does not distinguish science from other fields of human endeavor. In fact, the historian, the archeologist, the musicologist all use not only common sense but the same criteria for truth, correlation, and consistency. Perhaps all one can really say in very general terms about the scientific method is that, as in the method for all other subjects, certain rules dictated by intelligence and sound judgment must be observed.

There is a paradoxical view which is even closer to the heart of science. Albert Einstein said that common sense is a layer of prejudices laid down in the mind prior to the age of eighteen. As we have just emphasized, it is indeed true that many of the important advances in science are outside our experience. They concern objects too small or too large, so that, if anything, our experience becomes an impediment to our easy understanding, and we must learn we can no longer trust our senses with the commonplace information they provide. Then we must rely entirely upon the facts and the deductions from the facts and set aside all questions of whether or not the results of the inquiry seem reasonable to us based upon our past experience.

The formal approach to science is founded upon a scientific method which is a set of rules that comply with common sense. This has become the province of philosophy, and the philosophers have devised a grammar of scientific usage which, in its pure form, is a scientific method. This is sometimes called the philosophy of science, and various approaches have specific names, such as logic, logical positivism, symbolic logic, and others. But it must be clear from the very beginning that these approaches are no more science than the English language or mathematics. They are ways of expressing scientific information so that their consistency can be as perfect as possible. The meaning of words, the meaning of sentences can be loose or general, or it can be precise even to the extent of being expressed by mathematical formulas. The process of combing out the confusion and inconsistencies in the words and the construction of the thought sequence is the scientific method of the philosopher of science. He does not make scientific discoveries or even discuss the generalizations of science themselves; he tries to purify and perfect the tools of communication: the meaning of words, the grammar of sentences, the logic of thought sequences, precise statement of what is assumed and what is known, precise understanding of the distinction between matters of faith and value judgments on the one hand and matters of incontestable facts on the other. Sometimes his analysis may ask some rather general questions about the thought process, such as what is an explanation? what is proof?

Clearly logic is a subject that should be known to all scientists, but it is not one that is necessary in order to make a scientific discovery or to understand one. Some will argue that if a scientist does not use the language of a logician to express his science, he is equivalent to being illiterate. If this is the case, however, the vast majority of scientists are illiterate. Furthermore, if someone expresses his science in perfect logical form, while it is no doubt more precise, it is less easy to understand; in fact, to most nonphilosophers it is positively obscure, just as mathematical expression is hard for the nonmathematician. But fortunately the study of logic is of great assistance in training one's common sense, and one can use to advantage many of its lessons without having to become a total philosopher as well as a scientist.

Having said that science is not philosophy, it leaves us with the question of what, in fact, is it? This whole book is really an answer to that question. It is a question that could be answered many ways, and here we shall concentrate on one.

Science is about things. It is about rocks, stars, atoms, and living beings. It is about all those things which surround us and which used to be called Nature with a capital N. Furthermore, it is about the relation of things; science is concerned with order.

There are two ways we can deal with these *things*. The first and most obvious one is to describe them. Sometimes this is very easy and sometimes it is technically a most difficult problem, so that today there are many things about us that still need to be described and are actively being examined by scientists with this specific object in mind. We will return to these problems presently.

But description in itself is dissatisfying and insufficient. It is a large heap with no order to it. Finding the order in the descriptive facts is the great purpose of science. The making of generalizations—sometimes called theories, or laws, or principles—about facts is always considered the greatest triumph in the human pursuit of science.

These generalizations vary greatly in their character. Sometimes they are a simple classification of the facts. This serves to give some order to the heap, so that Nature appears to have a system. It is like taking a drawer full of loose stamps and putting them in an album so that they are arranged according to country and date. This is precisely what is done in mineralogy with the classification of minerals, in molecular biology in analyzing metabolic processes, and in biology in the classification of animals and plants. Classification among living organisms is generally thought to have been put on a firm basis by the Swedish naturalist Carl von Linné, who in the eighteenth century devised a simple method of classifying animals and plants. He called it the System of Nature. In point of fact many before him had done precisely the same thing, including Aristotle, but Linnaeus, as he is usually called, did it in a most comprehensive and successful way.

Generalizations in science are important or not depending upon whether they are satisfying to the human mind. One always imagines science to be absolute and complete within itself without any help from man. After all, the universe and the world existed along before man evolved. But what we know of the world and how we wish to think about it is by no means absolute; the concept is a creation of human intellect and human culture. If we say one generalization or law is more important than another, what we mean is that it is more important to us as people, for it gives us a greater inner feeling that we understand the world about us. There is no impartial test as to what makes a good generalization and what makes a poor one; for it is no more than a satisfaction of our own psychological needs.

For instance, it cannot be argued that the more general a generalization, the greater its importance. To say that everything that is not white is either black or colored may be a very general proposition, but it is also profoundly uninteresting. What then is the quality about scientific principles that makes them more or less satisfying? It seems to have something to do with tying up the loose ends and giving order where there was disorder. Making a list of animal and plant kingdoms is distinctly satisfying in a modest way.

Another important generalization, which amounts to a kind of classification, is the notion that all material objects are made up of atoms. This was a generalization which was first a speculation of the Greek philosophers, especially Democritus, but later, during the course of the nineteenth century, it became a firmly established principle of western science and the basis of atomic physics. In biology the discovery by Matthias Jakob Schleiden and Theodor Schwann in the middle of the nineteenth century that all organisms were composed of cells again provided a basis of structural classification of all organisms which is generally considered to be of great importance. As we will see further on, these notions have been instrumental in leading to further important facts and generalizations about matter and living things.

Many of the greatest generalizations in science have to do with change. We are deeply concerned about both the relationship between objects in nature and the consequence of this relationship during the course of time.

Consider, for instance, the kinetic theory of gases. This says that the movement of molecules is the physical basis for the three states, solid, liquid, and gas. The rate of movement of the molecules is related to temperature. For any one substance (for example, water), at low temperatures there will be little movement (ice), and as the temperature rises, in a liquid the molecules will be jostling about at greater speed (water), and in a gas they will be rushing about at furious pace (steam). The fact that the three states are so different structurally has to do not only with the effect of temperature on the velocity of the molecules, but their density, as well as the forces of attraction between them. This is one of the great generalizations of science: it relates the three states on the common basis of the activity of molecules. Furthermore it is a generalization which explains a change, in this case a change of physical states.

The laws of motion of Newton and the more modern laws of relativity of Einstein are considered two of the great achievements in science. Both are first and foremost laws of change and of the relationship between things. Even all the early speculation of the stars and the planets of Copernicus and Kepler are generalizations of change and relationship.

In biology it is generally agreed that two most important principles are the laws of heredity discovered by Mendel, and the theory of evolution by natural selection of Darwin. Mendelian principles show how offspring can vary systematically from parents in their characteristics; Darwinian evolution provides a hypothetical mechanism in natural selection which can steer the change of characteristics of individuals through the course of geological time, thereby giving a striking explanation to the fact that such change has occurred.

We could extend our list to equal and lesser generalizations, and even classify them in more precise ways, but that is not my purpose here. What has been said so far is that science describes the things in the universe about us and then makes generalizations with these descriptions. The generalizations are satisfying if they give a feeling of producing order and reducing mystery. Understanding change produced by interacting systems has more than anything else given us a feeling of learning what we want to know about Nature.

There is another way of looking at explanation in science that is very close to the heart of the method to be used in this book. Some scientists argue that the only way to explain or understand a phenomenon is to analyze it in its smaller units—to understand the living properties of the constituent molecules. To understand the living properties of organisms, one must know the chemical reactions which occur within an organism. The success of this method has been so remarkable that its importance can hardly be denied. Indeed we can understand crystal form in terms of the structure of the component molecules. Furthermore, from this knowledge we feel that the process of crystallization is essentially explained and no longer remains an outstanding problem of science. In the case of the infinitely more complex living systems, the recent advances of molecular biology or biochemistry have been so spectacular that we all feel there has been a large step forward in our understanding. The fact that we can pin genetic differences to specific structural changes in a chemical molecule within the cell is certainly an astounding and exciting discovery, and one which does describe and therefore explain larger events on a smaller level, in this case the molecular level. This micro-explanation approach to the analysis of the mysteries of science is known to the philosopher as *reductionism,* because it reduces the problem to its component parts and therefore to a lower level of size. One explains the molecular structure in terms of the structure of the atom, and so forth.

Recognizing the undeniable success of this approach, there are a number of scientists who feel that if one limits oneself to reductionism, some key characteristics of the system, whether it be a crystal, an organism, or a galaxy, will be lost. There are certain properties which go with the whole structure that can never be appreciated in terms of the component parts. Again this approach has a long history among philosophers and appears in various forms. The battle cry is that the whole is more than the mere sum of the parts; by coming together in a specific way, new unexpected properties emerge. Various names have been given to this concept, such as *holism, emergent evolution,* and *gestalt,* a term used in psychology. As an example, W. Koehler, who founded gestalt psychology, showed that we tend to see and hear things in groups, we do not merely add the component parts of impressions gained through our senses. Perhaps the most useful term of all to describe this approach to science is *organicism.* The *organismal approach* begins with the properties of the whole, and only has a secondary interest in the component parts. The fact that this term implies living organisms should not make it any less applicable to nonliving wholes, such as crystals, molecules, or clusters of stars, all of which can be considered in terms of the properties of their entirety instead of their subunits.

One of the principle reasons this second approach has been so important is that there are many complex systems—with living organisms a prime example—that seem beyond hope of being completely understood in terms of their parts. It is simply that there are too many parts, and this alone is used as an argument to show the difficulty of finding a total reductionist explanation. Even if one refuses to admit such an ultimate possibility, one is faced with the existing fact that in complex systems we do not presently have a complete explanation in the component parts. The antidote is to examine the properties of the whole, and from this one may derive two important benefits:

The first is to derive principles or laws which are characteristic of the larger level only. A prime example is that of quantum statistics. By considering masses of molecules, certain statistical properties emerge that are of vast importance within themselves. Another example would be in the study of ecology, where predictions about the increase or decrease of certain species of animal in a particular environment could not be made on the basis of the character of the animal. It is only in a study of all the factors in the whole environment that one can hope to understand the basis for any population changes. The result is that, depending upon the nature of the science, the organismal and the reductionist approaches play roles of varying importance.

The second benefit to be derived from organismal generalizations is that they are essential to show the reductionist where to attack. In many cases the problems themselves cannot be defined until an over-all look has been taken. The properties of crystals were known, described, and classified first, before they were understood in terms of molecular forces. The problem, so to speak, was set up in an organismal manner, and in this case the reductionist was able, successfully, to provide a molecular explanation. But this might not have been possible if the studies had been made in the reverse order.

Of all things, I do not wish to enter a philosophical controversy on these two approaches. It seems to me that despite our desire to put things in terms of antitheses, these two approaches are not opposed, but paired and equally essential to the progress of science. One must look up as well as down the scale, or else one is bound to be blind to some degree.

The particular importance to us of these two approaches lies in the fact that they concern size, and involve analysis at different levels of size. If we return now to the question of what is science, we have said that it is about things and that one can look at these things as either wholes or parts. We can string the things, the objects of science, in a size sequence, and this will give some order to the entire collection of things.

But it will do far more than that. We will not only spread out before us in a systematic way all the objects, but from the size sequence itself we will gain some insight into the structure of the entire universe. It is my contention that one of the most important aspects of all things is their size. Size alone has vast consequences in terms of the behavior of things. We can all think of homely examples and know, for instance, that birds must be small in order to be able to fly; a bird the size of a man could never manage. But here we are mainly concerned with much greater size differences than we see around us, differences which have correspondingly much greater consequences in the behavior and properties of the objects concerned.

One especially significant property is the speed of the objects and the relation of the speed to size. The curious fact is (as we shall see in detail presently) that the larger the object, such as a star, the more rapidly it moves; and, similarly, the smaller the object, such as a molecule, the more rapidly it moves. The world of our own experience lies in the middle of these two extremes. The things we can see easily with our own eyes have a size and a speed such that we can observe both, or at least come close to doing so. The living world is in between the world of planets and stars and the world of molecules and atoms.

This means that the things we can see most readily are living organisms, a fact not overly remarkable since we are organisms ourselves. With larger objects we use instruments, such as various types of telescopes, but soon, because of the distances of the objects and the limitations of the instruments, our information becomes less exact and we must speculate to an increasing extent as to the significance of what little we are able to see. With small objects we use various types of microscope, but soon the objects are way below our limit of resolution in size, and again we can no longer see them. In this case the ingenuity of instrumentation to obtain indirect information about shape, form, and velocity of movement has been perfectly amazing, but still we are very much in the dark as to the nature of some of these minute objects. The universe is full of things that are too big and too small for us to see. This does not mean that any one part is more important than the other; it simply means the world we see is but a minute fraction of all the existing-size worlds.

There is another aspect of the size levels besides velocity that is important. It is the change through time, or evolution. This is not a subject which we can see completely by looking at the universe today, but there are everywhere so many signs that the universe and the world are changing through time that we are constantly tempted to examine, discuss, and speculate in what direction this change has occurred and what are the causes of the change. Science therefore does not merely concern itself with the objects of different size at the present moment, but it concerns itself with their history as well.

Science, as we know it today, is subdivided into a number of disciplines, each with its own title. For instance, we have astronomy, biology, chemistry, geology, physics. Each of these is divided into various subdivisions; for instance, within biology we have ecology, genetics, physiology, biochemistry, and so forth. For the most part these different disciplines or subdisciplines apply solely at a particular size level, although there are some notable exceptions, such as physics, which cover a wide range.

As we proceed in our discussion of the different size levels, we will examine the disciplines involved. I will try to show, in a rough sort of way, what is known of the subject so far and what are the main unanswered questions. It will be an attempt to demonstrate the limitations of our present knowledge, and what questions the scientists in the field would really like answered next. Each subject at each size level has had different success in discovery in the past and a different store of unsolved problems. It must be possible to give a picture of the general kind of information we already know, and what we still need to know in order to have a more comprehensive picture. Sometimes the look will be according to a reductionist approach and sometimes up in an organismal approach. When we have laid this all out before us in its barest outline, then we can come back, in the final discussion, to see if indeed we do not have a better understanding of the nature of science.

2

FROM OUR POINT OF VIEW, THE MOST IMPORTANT aspect of the universe is its immensity. It is so large that the size is utterly meaningless to us. We can write it down, and even use the convenience of exponents (where $1,000,000 = 10^6$), but the figures are too large to be real. We have all stood outdoors on a clear night and looked at the canopy of stars and felt their beauty and the awe of the nothingness of the great space above us. But in terms of actual distance, all we can manage is that the stars are far away. So is China, yet we know they are farther than China. What we cannot intuitively grasp, without great intellectual effort on our part, is how unbelievably far away they are.

Even the units used in astronomical distances seem beyond our immediate comprehension. A light-year is the distance traveled by light in one year (365 days, or 8,760 hours, or 525,600 minutes, or 31,536,000 seconds). Light travels at approximately 186,300 miles per second (or 3×10^{10} centimeters per second). To picture this speed, the circumference of the earth is about 25,000 miles; it would take light less than 1/7 second to go about the world (were it possible to do so). A light-year is approximately 5.9×10^{12} miles (9.5×10^{17} centimeters), a distance which is indeed already too great to imagine.

If one light-year is too far to imagine, then what possible meaning can we derive from the fact that the farthest galaxy that can be observed with the most powerful telescope is estimated to be over two billion (2×10^9) light-years? Clearly the diameter of the entire universe must exceed this figure, but the distance is so large that making it any larger seems insignificant. Superlatives of the human mind have become utterly worn out.

The universe is an area of space which contains stars. The stars are not uniformly distributed in space, but they form clusters called galaxies, which are about 100,000 light-years in diameter. In the universe there are thought to be some 10^{15} galaxies, and each one of these contains on the average 10^8 stars. Not only are distances beyond comprehension, but numbers as well.

The galaxies themselves are not evenly spaced throughout the universe; they also tend to group. Therefore, the distance between galaxies varies considerably, and the average distance is about one million light-years.

To continue our size description of the universe, the stars within a galaxy are separated by an average distance of 5 light-years. We are part of a galaxy which we recognize as the Milky Way. Galaxies have many different forms, all presumed to be related to their movement, their rotation. They may be round, flattened ellipses, or spirals of different configurations, and in some cases they form rather irregular shapes. Our galaxy is a flattened spiral in which one of the stars, the sun, is about two-thirds away from center toward the edge. The fact that the Milky Way is a broad band across the sky is an index of the flatness of the spiral.

The stars themselves vary tremendously in size as well as in their degree of brightness. The sun has a diameter of 864,000 miles. There are stars that are much smaller (1/10 the mass of the sun) and some which are much larger (10,000 times the mass of the sun).

A Galaxy

AN enlargement of one minute speck of the previous plate of the universe.

This is an imaginary view of our own galaxy from many light-years away. The galaxy has a diameter of roughly 100,000 light-years and it contains about 2×10^{11} stars, of which one is the sun. The distance between the stars near the sun is in the order of 5 light-years, or in other words, the distance between stars is roughly 10 million times greater than their diameter.

A Star

A MINUTE part of our galaxy.

The sun is a star whose diameter is some 864,000 miles. There are a number of planets which orbit about the sun, and the innermost three are shown here. First is Mercury, which has a diameter of 3,010 miles and is about 40 million miles from the sun. The next is Venus, which has a diameter of 7,610 miles and is just over 67 million miles from the sun. The earth is the third one shown. Its diameter is 7,927 miles and it is almost 93 million miles from the sun.

A Planet

OUR planet, the earth, and the moon, which can be seen in the lower part of the plate. The earth has a diameter of 7,927 miles, the moon a diameter of 2,160 miles. The distance between the two varies somewhat because the orbit of the moon is elliptical; it averages about 235,000 miles.

Around each star there may be planets. The sun, for instance, has nine such planets, of which the earth is one. Planets are far smaller than stars, and they differ in their distance from their star, their rates of movement and rotation, their density, their chemical composition, their atmospheres, and in the number of satellites or moons that are in turn orbiting around them. In our solar system Jupiter is the largest planet, with a diameter of 86,000 miles, and Mercury the smallest, with a diameter of 3,100 miles. By comparison, the diameter of the earth is 7,918 miles and the moon 2,160 miles. Mercury is the planet closest to the sun, having a mean distance to the sun of 36 $\times$ 10^6 miles. The earth is the third planet from the sun, with a mean distance of 92.9 $\times$ 10^6 miles. Pluto is the farthest away, on the average 3,671 $\times$ 10^6 miles from the sun. Expressed in millions of miles, the moon is on the average 0.24 $\times$ 10^6 miles from the earth.

We have in this picture of the universe a whole series of size levels, beginning with the entire universe, then the clusters of galaxies, the galaxies themselves, the stars, and finally the planets. At each level it is striking that the units are not evenly spaced or randomly distributed, but clearly clustered. This applies to groups of galaxies, stars, and planets. We will examine the reason for this presently.

To round off this description of the universe, it may be helpful to list the size levels we have discussed in the form of a table, so that at a glance one can compare the different levels:

Mean distance	*Ratio between steps*
Diameter of universe: 10^{10} light-years (10^{23} miles)	
	10,000
Between galaxies: 10^6 light-years (10^{19} miles)	
	10
Diameter of a galaxy: 10^5 light-years (10^{18} miles)	
	100,000
Between stars: 5 light-years (10^{13} miles)	
	10,000
Between planets and stars: 10^9 miles	
	10
Diameter of stars: 10^8 miles	
	10,000
Diameter of planets: 10^4 miles	

But again the figures have little impact on our imagination. They do not give any appreciation of the immensity involved. A most vivid answer to this problem is presented by Robert Jastrow, who is the director of the Goddard Institute for Space Studies, in *Red Giants and White Dwarfs.** He says:

An analogy will help to clarify the meaning of these enormous distances. Let the sun be the size of an orange; on that scale of sizes the earth is a grain of sand circling in orbit around the sun at a distance of 30 feet; the giant planet Jupiter, 11 times larger than the earth, is a cherry pit revolving at a distance of 200 feet, or one city block; Saturn is another cherry pit two blocks from the sun; and Pluto, the outermost planet, is still another sand grain at a distance of ten city blocks from the sun.

On the same scale the average distance between the stars is 2000 miles. The sun's nearest neighbor, a star called Alpha Centauri, is 1300 miles away. In the space between the sun and its neighbors there is nothing but a thin distribution of hydrogen atoms, forming a vacuum far better than any ever achieved on earth. The galaxy, on this scale, is a cluster of oranges separated by an average distance of 2000 miles, the entire cluster being 20 million miles in diameter.

An orange, a few grains of sand some feet away, and then some cherry pits circling slowly around the orange at a distance of a city block. Two thousand miles away is another orange, perhaps with a few specks of planetary matter circling around it. That is the void of space.

We have before us now an oversimplified description of the universe and its major component parts. But it will be sufficient as a background for the important questions we wish to examine next. These center around the nature of our concern with these heavenly bodies: What have they told us so far about the fundamental nature of matter, what do we still want to know about them, and what is the future of astronomical science?

One aspect is obvious and not profound. A major contribution has been the measurement of all the aspects of the skies. This has included the perfection of optical telescopes and the elaboration of many different astronomical techniques including the recent development of radio telescopes. As one looks at the history of astronomy,

* Harper & Row, 1967.

it is the history of the increase of precision through this sort of technology. And obviously the limits of this kind of advance are still not in sight. We will accumulate many more facts about the stars, and as we do our views and theories will evolve correspondingly. The movements of the planets were first measured by the ancients; from their measurements came the interpretation of Ptolemy that the earth was the center of the universe and that everything revolved about it. With increased precision it was possible to show that the later theory of Copernicus was in fact correct. The final proof was made by Kepler, who used the exceptionally precise measurements of the astronomer Tycho Brahe.

In recent years the measurements have concerned themselves especially with the most distant stars and galaxies with a hope of improving our understanding of the nature of the universe itself. What are its limits, what are its borders? From this inquiry a particularly interesting fact has emerged.

In observing the most distant stars it can be shown that the light they emit is shifted toward the red end of the spectrum. This is interpreted to be a result of the Doppler effect, the well-known phenomenon which is so easily demonstrated with sound waves. A whistle on an approaching train will have a rising tone, compared to the falling tone on a receding train, if it is traveling at a good rate. The reason is that the waves are compressed while the distance between the observer and the source is being shortened, and vice versa. If this is the explanation of the red shift of the galaxies, then one may calculate the direction and the rate of movement of the galaxy. In all cases the distant galaxies appear to be moving away from us, and what is more surprising, the more distant the galaxy, the faster it recedes, as can be seen from the table given below.

Galaxy	Distance in light-years	Rate of moving away in miles per second
Virgo	7,500,000	750
Ursa Major	100,000,000	9,300
Corono Borealis	130,000,000	13,400
Bootes	230,000,000	24,400
Hydra	350,000,000	38,000

This information is the basis for much cosmological speculation. One of the most accepted cosmological theories is known as the Big Bang hypothesis. It presumes that a gigantic explosion occurred some 10 billion years ago and that what we see in the above figures is simply the continued expansion of the universe as a result of the explosion. This does not specify the shape of the universe, although it assumes some sort of sphere. Nor does it (or any other theory) say what lies beyond this sphere of galaxies; this is a matter of total conjecture.

The fact that science is man-made has no better illustration than in astronomy. When Copernicus suggested that the earth was not the center of the universe, his view was simply considered heretical and Galileo suffered by defending it. At that time man was considered to be the center of everything, and to have the planets revolve around some other structure seemed a great blow to our collective ego. The Big Bang hypothesis is another example. Many have found it vaguely depressing to think that ultimately the universe may diffuse into nothing. Comfort appears in the form of hypotheses which involve the cycling of movements, the idea being that at some later period the distant galaxies will come rushing back. The fact that some less distant galaxies do not appear to be moving away has been used as evidence to support this hypothesis. It is not my purpose here to present the detailed evidence for either hypothesis, but rather to stress the distressing psychological effect of the Big Bang theory. Yet if we look at the matter rationally, we must see that any degradation of the universe could not occur before trillions of years, many billions of years after the earth is no longer habitable in any event. It would seem to make more sense to worry about the fate of our children and grandchildren rather than our descendants many millions of generations from now.

Astronomy has another important lesson for us. It has to do with the exceptional size of the objects and the distances which have had a most important consequence in our scientific thinking. The laws of motion of Isaac Newton are considered the cornerstone of physics; all our basic understanding of mechanics comes from these laws. It is now known, from the work of Albert Einstein on relativity, that these laws of Newton are only rough approximations and that much more sophisticated and abstract methods are needed for a true understanding of the nature of motion. One might well ask why we continue to teach and think in terms of the simplified Newtonian terms if they are essentially incorrect. The answer is related to size.

If we are concerned with objects close to our size range, the Newtonian principles apply, for the discrepancies are so small that they are not detectable. The difference comes only when one is concerned with the vast distances in the universe. Then our basic concept of space, time, mass, and energy must be altered so that we can move accurately and cope realistically with huge phenomena. A small discrepancy will become a sizable error if the size is greatly magnified.

The basic concepts of relativity are highly abstract and for most of us these concepts are exceedingly difficult to grasp, since even when they are grasped, one has the sensation that they have been learned by rote and that one has no feeling for the new thought. The mathematician who enjoys abstraction has the psychological advantage that he can enjoy the new abstraction as one might enjoy a difficult move in a game of chess. The fact that relativity is removed from experience makes it if anything more exciting to him; it is like entering the unknown of a deep, unexplored cave. The mathematician can see the beauty of it and he can see how one is led to all these wonderful new insights into nature. But the poor, ordinary, nonmathematical citizen sees none of the process—only the result, which appears unreal and unlikely, to put it mildly. No amount of reading of "relativity made easy" will produce any feeling of pleasure with the new method and the new results. The pleasure comes only if you are born with an ability to abstract and can see the steps through from beginning to end in your own mind.

We must now turn our attention to the question of how stars and planets might have been formed. As before, there is a certain amount of precise data which is obtainable from the heavens with ingenious instruments. The data are interpreted in some form of consistent hypothesis. But the fact that it is a hypothesis cannot be too strongly emphasized. Even with no new facts, some clever person may come up with a better one. But there will be new facts as astronomers keep observing and measuring, and the hypotheses must keep pace with the facts. One of the reasons we must always remain content with hypotheses is that we are dealing with a historical event that occurred over billions of years. We have no way of proving what happened so many years ago; there was no observer there who left us a notebook with a record. This property of the uncertainty of past events is a common attribute of many parts of science besides astronomy, especially in geology in the reconstruction of earth history and in the related problems in biology of the evolution of plants and animals.

The first and foremost factor in the present configuration of the universe is the force of gravity, another well-known contribution of the great Isaac Newton. This is a real force, very much weaker than the forces which exist within the atom, yet it is sufficient to keep the moon orbiting about the earth, and the earth orbiting around the sun. Gravitation does more, however, than explain the clustering of planets about a star; it also accounts for the clustering of stars into galaxies and even the grouping of galaxies. The fact that matter is not uniformly spaced throughout the universe but clotted in various regions is entirely due to the force of gravity.

It is imagined that originally space consisted of hydrogen atoms wandering about in clouds. These clouds, by accident, might accumulate to a significant degree in a particular region, and this sudden chance concentration of hydrogen might be sufficiently vast and dense so that, instead of flying away as they had come, the hydrogen atoms would be held together by gravitational force. Furthermore, this force would actively pull the hydrogen atoms to a central point so that the cloud would begin to contract. As the contraction occurred, it is postulated, the hydrogen atoms picked up speed as they moved inward. This increase in energy would give rise to an increase in temperature.

Great temperatures play a key role in the evolution of stars. They first cause the hydrogen to loose its electrons so that a "plasma" arises of dislocated electrons and protons. The contraction continues and the temperature rises to millions of degrees, temperatures sufficient to cause the protons to fuse, with the release of nuclear energy as in the explosion of a hydrogen bomb. As a result of such an explosion, the mass emits light and becomes visible as a star. This nuclear reaction leads to a balance between the inward pull of gravity and the outward thrust of the explosions. It is of interest to note that in discussing immense stars, we have suddenly dropped to a minute level, that of the atom. Physics is one subject that deals with problems at all size levels, and here in one sweep it encompasses the stars in terms of the atoms, the constituent parts. Stars, like other physical systems, are relatively homogeneous and made up of few component parts. In most of the life of a star, despite its great size, it is composed entirely of hydrogen and helium. Its internal structure is not complex, but rather it contains an incredibly large number of similar minute component parts. Later, through the fusion of nuclei at very high temperatures, other elements are formed.

A star is not a permanent, perpetual equilibrium, for stars disappear as well as appear. The first sign of senescence is a great swelling and a red glow, producing what is known as a "red giant." Following this red stage the star will again contract and produce even higher temperatures. If the star is small it will become an intensely illuminated "white dwarf," which will eventually cool and lose its light. The fate of large stars is far more interesting. They will produce further elements by additional nuclear fusions at even greater temperatures as the successive contractions alternate with periods of expansion. The last stage is one gigantic nuclear explosion, which disperses all the matter (in the form of all the elements) over great distances. The elements that exist on the earth today are derived from some early star that exploded. The explosions are called supernovas. They are occasionally observed along with subsequent clouds surrounding the area where the star once existed.

Hypotheses concerning the origin of the planets are somewhat less satisfactory than those connected with the birth of stars. One widely accepted view is that when stars form there are smaller satellite clouds of gas that condense alongside the star and that these clouds, because they are so small, fail to generate the heat necessary to create a luminous, nuclear-reacting star. According to such a scheme, the planets, including earth and the moon, arose together and at the same time. There are, however, problems to such a hypothesis and it is to be expected that with new information, we will have improved and more consistent theories as to the origin of the earth and its main satellite.

The study of the planets has begun a wholly new and exciting phase, largely because of the advent of space rockets. Already we have new knowledge of the moon, and by the next decade we should know very much more. Furthermore the atmospheres and the composition of the other planets in our solar system are even more intriguing, and we have some new information on the surface structure of Mars taken by photographs from a rocket.

But there are more homely aspects of planets which are of great importance and have numerous consequences. One such is the tides. The pull of gravity exerts a force on water, and since ocean water can move, it does so in the form of tides. In our case, the moon's proximity causes our tides, although the sun also exerts a slight effect. Because of the inertia of large bodies of water, tidal movement lags some hours behind the moon's passage, and the amount and the timing of the rise and fall in any one locality depend to a large extent on the local patterns of the bays and peninsulas. The moon does more than pull the water toward it, for the surface of the earth is slightly deformable also. These land tides mean that there is a slight bulge in the direction of the moon (making the earth more elliptical), but the extent of such movement is very small, a mere 10-inch rise and fall of the earth's crust. Tides as well as the regular appearance and disappearance of the moon and the sun have far-reaching effects on the activities of living creatures on the face of the earth. The activities of most animals and plants are on a daily rhythm, which is to some degree controlled by the direct rays of the sun, or on a lunar rhythm, which is controlled by the reflected rays of the sun off the moon. But we are anticipating our story.

Another planetary subject of great interest is the chemical composition of planets. This concerns not only the surface chemicals, but also those of the gaseous atmosphere. In the past twenty years the study of our own atmosphere and its many layers has played an important part in the technical advance of communication (because of the radio-wave reflecting properties of some layers), rocketry, and, of course, meteorology. There is even at the moment a science of planet meteorology, which extends to all the planets of the solar system.

We would also like to know all about the interior of the planets, but obviously this presents difficulties. It is possible to gain information on the density of planets, but this says little about interior composition. We do not even have good ways of looking into the center of our own planet, and end up by making all sorts of guesses based upon indirect observations. For instance, the deflection of tremors caused by earthquakes tells us about concentric change in composition, and one can make further deductions from other sources as to density and even chemical composition. These are hypothetical, but they fit the facts and are generally accepted. The earth is known to have (like a golf ball) a central core made up of dense liquid; it is some thousands of degrees in temperature. Because of the density, it is presumed that this merely contains much iron under very high pressure. As a matter of fact, it has been shown that the core is made up of two parts; the inner and the outer. The largest mass of the earth consists of the next layer, which is the mantle. This layer is of intermediate density and comes right up under the superficial crust. It would be of great interest to know its composition, and no doubt the day will soon come whereby a direct sample will be obtained by drilling.

The fruits of these labors, although of tremendous interest, are not likely to lead to significant generalizations. It is true that in recent years there has been an increase in interest in geophysics, which is the application of physical principles to the study of the insides of the earth. In this case, theoretical considerations concerning the nature of matter are applied to the structure and composition of the interior unknowns of our planet. It is too early to predict in

46 *The Scale of Nature*

this case whether or not new principles will emerge, but the descriptions of what we cannot see directly should become increasingly detailed and closer to the truth as time goes on.

We have, in this short chapter, taken a gigantic excursion through space: from the edge of the enormous universe to the center of a small planet. The questions to be answered are as immense as the objects, and the techniques for answering these questions will be twofold: the development of sophisticated equipment to measure and probe, and the use of the most abstract mathematics to make workable models that are consistent with the ever-increasing new facts. Both approaches are precise and mathematical; one is experimental and the other is theoretical.

The Crust

3

IN OUR CONTINUOUS SWING FROM LARGER TO smaller objects, we are no longer considering a whole planet but only a small part of it, a small segment of the crust of our earth. The crust is something we can touch, see, and examine in all its fine detail. The size level allows us to make a complete set of direct observations. There are some things which still require indirect deductions, but these are largely the reconstruction of past changes in the crust which have taken millions of years to occur and therefore are too slow rather than too large to be observed. For the most part, the geologist with his hammer or his drill can bring the rocks directly into the laboratory and analyze them quite exhaustively. With this information he may build geological maps that show the distribution of the minerals throughout whole areas. The maps may be three-dimensional, so that not only is the surface known but also all the layers some distance below the surface. Conjecture creeps in only if he now wishes to show how the present crust structure arose from past structure. But even here he has so many guide lines that on most points there is general agreement as to the sequence of events. The science of earth crust, geology, is one in which we have an extensive knowledge. There remain some important and intriguing problems, as we shall see, but geology is a science which on the whole has reached its maturity.

The direct mapping of the rocks of the world, at least in its broad outlines, is largely accomplished. Africa and other remote areas have received careful examination only in recent years, and there remains much to be done, but there is no anticipation of any major surprises. A more recent frontier has been the mapping of the bottom of the oceans. Again many more details need to be known, but the principal observations have been made. The unknowns are commensurate with their depth; both the bottom of deep troughs in the ocean and way under the crust everywhere remain unexplored regions.

There are two principal aspects of the geology of the crust. One is the analysis of the rocks themselves and the other is earth history.

The study of rocks, or mineralogy, is really a branch of chemistry. It concerns not only the nature of the substances within the rock, whether it be a compound of silicon, iron, magnesium, and so forth, but also the state in which the substance exists. The majority of minerals are true crystals and therefore within the domain of the crystallographers. We are not at the right size level yet to consider anything so small as the molecular structure of crystals, but here I merely want to emphasize that again a large structure, such as the crust of the earth, is analyzed in minute terms, namely, those of molecules and how the molecules pack together. To some degree there is an intermediate level here, the form of the crystal itself, but this form is always strictly interpreted in terms of molecular forces and the resulting packing.

But mineralogy involves far more than crystals, for often rocks are made up of a mixture of different crystals which can be arranged in a wide variety of patterns. These patterns depend upon the manner in which the rock was formed, and rocks in general are classified as igneous, sedimentary, and metamorphic. Igneous rocks are formed

The Earth's Crust

THIS is a view of the western portion of North America. It covers an area of about 100,000 square miles, largely of the mountain formations of the Rockies.

directly from the molten state and are generally made up of many fine crystals; granite is an example. Sedimentary rocks result from the packing down of sand, gravel, and rock fragments, or even the crystallizing out of minerals from solution. These may be layered and compacted, as is often evident in limestone or sandstone, which are typical sedimentary rocks. Metamorphic rocks are the result of old rocks being reheated under pressure. A good example is marble, which comes from heated limestone. The partial liquefying causes the small crystals of limestone to realign and produce the larger crystals of marble. There is no change in the chemical composition during the process, but merely a reorganization of the fine structure.

Because each of these types of rock has a different mode of formation, it is possible to get some insight into the past history of a region of the crust by simply analyzing the distribution of the different types of rock. The evidence that sedimentary rock comes from the layering is written directly in the rock itself. The process of the formation of rock under heat and pressure is still being examined in the laboratory, where attempts are being made to imitate the high temperature and pressure found below the surface of the earth.

Another kind of analysis that has been made of the earth crust is on an even smaller, or more micro, level. This is the analysis of the chemical substances of which the rocks themselves are composed. The compounds are numerous, but if the chemicals are expressed in terms of elements, oxygen is the most abundant, followed by silicon, aluminum, iron, calcium, sodium, potassium, magnesium, and many others which exist in minute amounts.

So far we have dwelt upon the nature of rocks themselves, a subject which is the backbone of geology, but one which has been well known for some years despite some intriguing mysteries which remain. Let us now turn to larger questions, namely, the movement of parts of the crust up or down, which have caused changes in its contours. That such changes have occurred has been known for many years; in fact, it could not be more evident. I remember as a young boy climbing in the Swiss Alps and stopping to rest on top of a small mountain. I put my knapsack on a rock and beside it saw a beautifully symmetrical fossil starfish embedded in the rock. Starfish do not climb mountains, so some years later when I took a course in geology I did not need any convincing that land may rise great distances, from the bottom of the oceans to the top of the mountains.

One of the important remaining problems of geology is to explain these massive movements of the earth crust. It is known that a few of them can be explained by the activities of volcanoes. Indeed, there are well-known cases where a whole mountain or, more recently, near Iceland, a whole island appeared in a few years, where none existed before. But these eruptive blisters on the crust are special and account for only a small percentage of the upthrusts. And even they still contain mysteries as to how and why they form. Another even less important way of producing rises is the formation of coral islands. As Charles Darwin showed, corals deposit calcareous shells, which cause a progressive growth, slowly rising over the course of many years until it reaches the surface of the sea. The more important movements, which may even form whole mountain ranges, are called diastrophic movements. Their cause is unclear, and many factors are thought to contribute. One old, obsolete view is that the earth is known to be cooling slowly, and over many years some surface contraction might be expected. A more modern theory is that a change in the rotation of the earth's axis might cause disturbances in the crust. A frequently expressed idea, and one of considerable interest at the moment, is that the continents are drifting, again as a result of the earth's rotation, and this drift causes the foldings and bunchings of the surface. There are other theories, but none is considered to be in any way definitive.

It is naturally assumed that changes in the form of the crust are related to earthquakes. The fact that earthquakes occur with greater frequency in certain regions of the globe than in others is interpreted as indicative that those regions are ones of significant change at the moment. Other evidences that such changes are occurring in our era can be seen on some coastlines, where the shoreline is either receding or rising gradually over the years. This is not caused by a change in the level of the ocean, but by the movement of the land. Scandinavia and the New England coast are slowly rising, and it has been suggested that they rise because they have been relieved of the great ice masses of the glaciers from the last ice age. We therefore have yet another factor which could influence the diastrophic movements.

Factors which wear down plateaus or peaks are much easier to understand. Erosion is a straightforward process and can be observed in its various stages everywhere. Most commonly erosion is by water, but glaciers also erode, the rivers of ice leaving special U-shaped valleys.

One might think of the history of the earth's crust then as a series of buckling thrusts constantly worn down by erosion. The geologist is not only concerned with the mechanism of these changes, but with their history as well. He wants to be able to describe the earth's crust from the very beginning to the present and be able to explain the reasons for all the changes. For a description of past events, he has been greatly helped by the existence of fossils, which give a time sequence to many sedimentary rock formations that have proved invaluable in interpreting past sequences. Recently, he has the further effective tool of radioactivity. Because it is known how long it takes atoms to change from one radioactive form (isotope) to another, it is possible to date rocks with this atomic clock with an accuracy hitherto quite unknown.

One of the principal conclusions that comes from these historical studies is how remarkably long it has taken these changes to occur. It is estimated that the earth is 4.5 billion years old. Abundant fossils of plants and animals began to appear half a billion years ago, although the earliest cells of presumed bacteria have been found in rocks about 3 billion years old. While these estimated times are only small fractions of the times involved in major changes in galaxies, they are nevertheless so long that they have little reality in terms of our own sense of time.

A Community

4

THERE IS NO QUESTION BUT THAT ONE OF THE most interesting aspects of the earth's crust is the fact that it supports life. It is, of course, not merely the properties of the crust itself that make this possible, but the surrounding atmosphere as well. The presence of oxygen, carbon dioxide, and water vapor has a key significance for the essential energy-converting process of living organisms. Most animals and plants consume oxygen and as a product of their internal combustion give off carbon dioxide and water. In the daytime photosynthetic plants, with the energy of the sun, do the reverse; they consume carbon dioxide and water, converting them into energy containing compounds such as sugars, and these compounds are directly or indirectly the fuel for all organisms on the face of the earth. Therefore, without the sun and the earth's particular atmosphere there could be no life as we know it. There are, however, other possible means of storing and obtaining energy, and these alternatives are being seriously examined in the general problem of whether or not life exists on other planets.

55

A Community

A VIEW from a peak down into a valley of the Rocky Mountains. This valley supports an intricate community of many different species of animals and plants.

Besides moisture, sunlight, and the atmospheric gases, temperature is another quality of the earth's surface that plays a significant role in determining what kind of living creatures may exist in any one area. On a crude level, it is evident that there are relatively few organisms that live in the polar regions, while by contrast the tropics have a great abundance. Not only that, but in the temperate zones there are great seasonal fluctuations in temperature, and this in turn has a significant effect on the number and the kinds of organisms. Temperature difference may also be the result of altitude, and again it is not surprising to discover that the fauna and flora change as one goes up a mountain.

The study of the geographical distribution of animals and plants is an old yet continually active field. One of the pioneers was Alfred Wallace, the naturalist who along with Darwin propounded the theory of natural selection in the middle of the last century. Today one of the pressing problems facing the ecologist, who concerns himself with such matters, is the question of the causes of diversity. By diversity is meant the number of species in any one region, and it is well known that in any one kind of habitat, land or aquatic, the number of species in a given area decreases as one proceeds to the poles. It may also be that the total number of individuals decreases, although this has been considered a relatively less important matter. The reason that greater stress is put on species diversity is that it bears upon the whole question of why there should be different species, and what are the factors which lead to species formation. We will return to this key matter shortly, for it is at the heart of the problem of the mechanism of evolution.

In our attempt to consider matters of ever-decreasing size, we can turn now from questions of global geographic distribution of organisms to those of a discrete region. This is sometimes called a community, and by this is meant a group of animals and plants that are living in the region in concert. It does not and cannot mean that this area is necessarily completely isolated from others, but it may be so to a mild degree, such as the isolation provided by a valley surrounded by mountains.

The Scale of Nature

One of the striking things about a community is that, provided there are no cataclysms such as a volcanic eruption, the animals and plants live in a stable relation to one another. This is popularly called the balance of nature, and the ecologists have, over the years, spent much time analyzing the nature of this equilibrium.

The basic consideration has been the use or flow of energy. If there are numerous animals and plants in a valley community which are continually consuming energy to keep warm, to move, and to permit growth synthesis, then the first rule is that the amount of photosynthesis that takes place among the green plants of the valley must be sufficient to support all the energy-consuming processes of the plants themselves and all the activities of the animals. But the fact that the amount of photosynthesis is sufficient is self-evident, and in fact an inverted way of looking at the matter. For what happens, since organisms are foremost opportunists, is that the amount of energy consumed depends on the amount available; the amount of photosynthesis sets a limit on the number of energy-consuming organisms that will be permitted to survive in a community. Along with this exchange and balancing of energy, there is a corresponding exchange and balancing of certain chemicals. Oxygen, hydrogen, nitrogen, and carbon go through cycles in which they are bound in different forms, and during the course of these cycles there is a steady supply of oxygen available for respiration, a supply of carbon dioxide available for photosynthesis, and a supply of carbon, nitrogen, and hydrogen available for the construction of sugars, proteins, and the other basic chemical constituents of living protoplasm. We can, therefore, talk of the equilibrium set up within a community in terms of the overall energy available, or in terms of the cycles of chemical constituents, but fortunately it is possible to look at the matter in ways more penetrating and interesting than this.

Some animals live on plants, while other animals are predators and eat animals. From this simple fact it is possible to construct food chains in which the bottom of the chain will consist of animals that are vegetarians. These are eaten by some carnivores, which are in turn eaten by some other carnivores, which in turn are the prey to yet another carnivore. In the case of our valley community, small plant-sucking insects might be the prey of larger insects or spiders, which are fed upon by insectivorous birds, which are preyed upon by hawks. One might construct another chain consisting of beetle grubs which feed upon the roots of various plants, which in turn are eaten by moles, which may be eaten by weasels, or hawks, or even coyotes. These food chains will often crisscross if the diet of one of its members is not strict and crosses over to include species which are also members of other food chains. One interesting characteristic is that as one goes up the chain, the individual animals become in general larger; a predator is likely to be larger than its prey. Also the number of large predators is less than the number of prey. The obvious reason for this again has to do with the supply of energy; if there were more predators than prey they would soon starve. Because of this requirement the food chain is sometimes described as a pyramid of numbers.

Some interesting studies have been done on the relation of the numbers of a prey and its predators. It can be shown from purely mathematical considerations that this equilibrium may, at any time, begin to oscillate, producing fluctuations in both the population of prey and, lagging behind, the population of predators. This is a well-known phenomenon, and the study of what factors affect the cycling of numbers continues to be of active interest to ecologists.

Certain organisms seem to be completely removed from the prey-predator chain. They are the large trees and the large herbivores, such as elk. Apparently great size is a protection against predation, but then these large organisms are no more protected than small ones against the infestations of small parasites. But fortunately it is characteristic of most parasites that they do not kill their host, presumably because this would mean their destruction as well. Rather they also stay in equilibrium, but in this case the size roles are reversed and the prey is in general larger than the predator.

In analyzing communities, the ecologist has looked for some order, some system to their organization. It is too crude to say simply that some organisms are prey and some are predators, or some are herbivorous, some carnivorous, and some photosynthetic. Finer and more revealing distinctions are needed. The concept of ecological niche has begun to fulfill this need, although there remain many difficulties and the matter has not been fully resolved. By niche is meant the place in nature of the organism. This place may be more than simply being a carnivore, or a herbivore, but may refer to a very specific diet. For instance, hummingbirds, moths, and bees eat the nectar of flowers. The presence of flowers produces a source of available food, and these food slots, or niches, are filled. Not all flowers are the same, but depending upon color and structure, one flower may make nectar available to a small bee, another to the thin beak of a hummingbird, and a third to the long proboscis of a moth. These are, therefore, at least three niches among the nectar feeders, and these are filled by three different kinds of animals.

Immediately one can say two things about niches within a community. Obviously, with an increase in the number of species, there will be correspondingly more niches. For instance, if there were no flowering plants but only ferns and mosses in the habitat, then there would be no nectar and, therefore, no nectar-eating insects and birds. In fact, if one uses the concept of niche in its most minute and restricted sense, one might say that the number of niches will equal the number of species. But the important emphasis, and in fact the value of the concept of the niche, is that it pinpoints the function, the activity, of the organism within its environmental community. It designates what the animal or plant does rather than what it looks like. This means that a community may be thought of as a collection of different activities which are interrelated and closely integrated. Furthermore, there are simple communities and complex ones, and in the latter each general function, such as eating, seems to be subdivided in numerous different ways, so that there may be such fine distinctions as three major, different modes of consuming nectar. There are also, of course, rather generalized eaters that have less specific diets, but even then it is unlikely that two species of omnivores will compete for the same unspecialized diet.

It is presumed that communities were not always complex, but they have become so during the course of time. This means that in any one community there must at one time have been fewer species than there are at present. It means, if we return to our example of nectar feeders, that not only at one time was there presumably only one kind of animal that fed on nectar rather than three, but at an even earlier time there must have been none, and in fact no nectar or even any flowering plants. The ability to produce nectar, which attracts animals and permits the fertilization of the plant, as well as the ability to eat the nectar must have arisen together. It is this marvelous fact which makes the study of ecology so vitally important, for through it we may reach a better understanding of one of the more remarkable processes of the world, the process of the evolution of living organisms.

The dimension that we are concerned with here is, with respect to distance, the width of a valley, but in time we have various possibilities. We could consider the changes that occur within the cycle of a day and a night, or the cycles that occur within a year-long change of seasons, or we could think of the changes that take place over 50 or 100 years. As we said before, this community is to a large degree in equilibrium and, therefore, the diurnal and seasonal changes tend to go through regular cycles and the community returns to approximately its original condition after a set period. The changes over a space of years may be appreciable, but they are only a hint of what occurs if one looks at the valley over spans of time involving millions of years. If one looks across great periods of time, then one may see the steps of evolutionary progress.

The evidence that such changes have occurred is sound. As we said before, in discussing the earth's crust, the story is largely told in the rocks. The fossils are embedded there, and by various methods, including the radioactivity of the rocks, it is possible to pinpoint the time of the living existence of the fossil. In this way one can reconstruct at least some of the more obvious inhabitants of the valley back to the Cambrian epoch, some 500 million years ago. We know the sequence of the different kinds of animals and plants and we know that with time they increased in size and complexity. This sequence is the preoccupation of the paleontologist and the paleo-botanist, who are trying to fit the pieces of this puzzle together. It is a slow and painstaking job, for the information is fragmentary and uneven, yet through years of careful study our knowledge of early life on earth is remarkably detailed. Paleontologists of today are beginning to look at all sorts of sophisticated subjects, such as the ecology of primeval habitats and the weather conditions of early eras as reflected in the vegetation. These studies are not directly analyti-cal in that they do not concern themselves immediately with the nature of matter and life; rather they are historical. But from them vital information has already come—vital, that is, to the analysis of the nature of living organs. The central fact, of course, is the over-whelming evidence that evolution has occurred.

The question of how evolution is achieved is one in which there remain some unresolved problems. The hypothesis of natural selec-tion put forth by Alfred Wallace and especially by Charles Darwin in his *Origin of Species,* published in 1859, had a stupendous and immediate success because it suggested a mechanism where pre-viously evolution appeared almost impossible to explain. In natural selection, since individuals vary in some fixed or heritable fashion, those variants that are more successful in flooding the population with their offspring are, by definition, the ones favored by selection. Selection means reproductive success or reproductive contribution to the subsequent generations. Since the characteristics which are re-sponsible for the success are inherited, they are passed on to the offspring, which in turn may vary and even further winnow the less successful characteristics which produce a reduced number of off-spring. This is not quite the form in which the concept of natural selection was expressed by Darwin, but by expressing it in terms of reproductive success it avoids certain confusions that are of historical rather than scientific interest.

But what we have said so far of natural selection hardly seems enough to account for changing our valley with perhaps one or two species in an early geological period into the vastly complex single community of today, containing great numbers of species all interrelated in complex ways. How is this transition possible? If we assume that our first few species were especially successful at producing many offspring, why is the valley not totally overrun with those forms that seemed only to be concerned with making more of themselves? The hypothetical argument to counter this contention is that by selection each species changes through time, and by changing, it alters its ecological relations with other species. What meant reproductive success in one period may not be the same in another, for the whole environment changes. But still this would not mean more species; what are the forces which would increase the number of species?

Any one species exists in and exploits a niche. It may do so inefficiently so that not all the resources of the niche are used. If a similar species which shares the niche appears on the scene and makes use of the untapped resources, then the two species can coexist in harmony. The presence of two species may cause modification of the niche itself if it is made up in part of living organisms, and such modification may result in the coming of other species so the three or even more noncompetitive species may live together. This is precisely what one sees in our example of different types of flowers producing nectar and different types of nectar eaters. With the passage of time, exploitation seems to be more complete if the number of niches and the corresponding number of species is raised to the saturation point for any one environment. The saturation point in turn is governed to some extent by the climate and the physical terrain in which the community lies.

These suggested mechanisms still leave much to be explained. In the past, ecologists have made repeated attempts to imitate one aspect of the environment in the laboratory, but the results more often than not are different from those in nature. For instance, two species may coexist in the wild, but they fail utterly to do so in the laboratory. This raises a major problem for the biologist: What is it about the natural environment which confers the stability so obviously missing in the laboratory?

The next key question is how does evolution work in the complex environment? As we shall see in the next chapter, many of our accepted models for evolution come from population genetics, which concerns single populations in artificial uniform conditions; perhaps the greatest challenge for the future lies in extending these considerations so that the evolutionary changes in a complex environment can be analyzed and understood.

5

WE HAVE NOW NARROWED THE VIEW FROM A
whole community to one species. The study of populations is
an older science than the study of communities, and for that reason
we know much more about populations. The work has centered
about the genetic constitution of the populations. In recent years
there has also been an interest in various aspects of behavior in animal populations, for it has been increasingly clear that the population is more than a mere collection of individuals but is integrated
in various interesting ways as a unit.

One of the best understood aspects of populations is their mechanism of inheritance: how the characteristics are passed along in the
population from generation to generation. Darwin recognized the
need for a mechanism of inheritance, but failed to arrive at an
acceptable one after prolonged study. It was one of the few failures of
Darwin's illustrious career. Gregor Mendel found the key during the
same period that Darwin was making his inquiry, but it was a quirk
of fate that Mendel's laws of heredity were not known to the world

until the beginning of the twentieth century even though they were published in 1866.

These laws said that characters were determined by discrete factors which usually existed in pairs. There were two significant facts about these pairs. If they were different, one (the dominant) could dominate the other (the recessive), so that the character to be seen in the offspring was of one parent only, even though it had the factor of both parents. The other significant fact was that these factors (at least the one Mendel was fortunate enough to choose) are independent of each other, that is, different combinations of them will occur in different offspring on a chance basis. It is now history (although it never loses its excitement) that others discovered the behavior of chromosomes during the formation of the sex cells (egg and sperm, or gametes), and that by 1903 it was finally realized that these factors, or genes, must lie on the chromosomes, and it was the chromosomes themselves which were sorting out in gamete formation. The chromosomes are threadlike bodies which lie in the nucleus. Each one contains many genes, and in the normal cells of the body the chromosomes are paired. At corresponding points in the chromosome pairs, one gene may differ from that of its twin (for example, one may be responsible for red flowers, the other white). The gametes have only one member of each chromosome pair, and it is obvious that a gamete might have either the chromosome with the red-flower gene or the one with the white-flower gene. If there is another pair of genes on another pair of chromosomes (for example, yellow and green seed), then they will also separate when the sex cells are formed. As a result one offspring might have a tendency toward white flowers and yellow seeds, or red flowers and green seeds, red flowers and yellow seeds, or white flowers and green seeds. Chance would determine which male sex cell (pollen) happened to fertilize which female sex cell (egg), and this is the modern understanding of Mendel's law of independent assortment. It should be added that if the two pairs of genes are on the same chromosome, they will not sort out but will remain together in the gamete (that is, they are linked).

There is one important exception to the above rule; there are

A Population

A HERD of elk (or wapiti) by a stream in the trough of the valley.

circumstances where even genes on the same chromosome can separate into different gametes. This is achieved by exchanges of parts of the chromosomes of the chromosome pair in gamete formation, a remarkable phenomenon known as crossing over. The chromosomes lie together like two strands of spaghetti, and both strands of the pair break in two at the same point. The front end of one strand now "crosses over" and joins with the hind end of the other (and vice versa), with the result that the new strands are made up of part of one chromosome and part of the partner. This phenomenon was discovered in the early part of this century at the beginning of what might be called the great era of genetics. If one looks at the list of those biologists who are recipients of Nobel Prizes for the last fifty years, the majority are geneticists. The progress in this field has been exciting and important, attracting the most brilliant minds. It is only now that there is some suspicion that the number of new discoveries of major significance is diminishing.

Another key discovery was that of mutation, or the sudden change of a character, for it was soon realized that all the shuffling in the world would not make new traits, but merely recombine the old ones that were already there. These discoveries were all made a long time ago, and the recent progress in genetics has been entirely on the level of the chemical basis of heredity, a matter which we shall consider when we arrive at the level of macromolecules.

Mutations produce the new traits and recombination shuffles the traits; variation is necessary for natural selection and evolution. There immediately ensued a raging argument (which can still be heard today) that it is impossible to conceive of evolutionary change in the simple terms of random mutation and recombination. If the complete modern theory of natural selection depends on this kind of variation, it is inadequate. How can something so beautiful, so complicated, so perfect as the mammalian eye ever have arisen by random mistakes of genes? The course of evolution has been (as the fossil record shows) from simple to complex, and therefore surely there must be some plan, some design, some as yet unknown force which directs the course of evolution. It need not be divine intervention, but surely it is more than random mutation. Scientists have on the whole treated such arguments with the utmost scorn. While they admit their scheme is no more than hypothesis, there is no reason to reject it because it does not fit in with one's intuitive feeling about the grandeur of Mother Nature. There are no facts which contradict the hypothesis. There is, furthermore, a great ally in the form of an immense amount of time. Undirected mutations may not produce much change in a time span within our own experience, but given millions of years, these minute changes can have a striking cumulative effect. And remember, according to the hypothesis, while the mutations are undirected, those that survive and those that are thrown away are directed by natural selection or reproductive success.

One of the important developments that occurred in the nineteen-thirties was an attempt to express evolutionary change in mathematical terms that used the simple genetic information as the basic currency. This so-called population genetics was developed primarily by R. A. Fisher and J. B. S. Haldane in England and Sewall Wright in this country. The basic procedure was very simple. It considered the rate of mutation and the rate of selection of certain characters—that is, the rate at which a gene would increase in frequency in a population. To this was added the size of the population and the number of generations. From relatively simple equations it could predict the changes in the genetic constitution of a given population in a given period of time. It concerned itself with gene pools within a population and the change of the gene pools over a period of time. As is so often the case with theoretical or mathematical approaches to problems, some wholly new ways of looking at evolutionary change emerged. Also much work was expended trying to test in the laboratory the conclusions reached from the mathematics; some of these tests were quite successful, while others were less so, presumably because by oversimplifying the problem the parallel to what occurs in nature becomes correspondingly remote. It is hoped that the new mathematical ecology will overcome this difficulty and provide further advances.

But as population genetics was being developed, the ecologists and the evolutionists were also busy looking further than the restricted equations. They reverted to the old questions of why and how new species form. Or to put it in terms of a population, how can one population, in which all the individuals can freely interbreed, become two populations in which there no longer can be cross-mating? The question of *why* this occurs is even more difficult, so let us concentrate on the *how* first.

There are a number of proposed mechanisms, but certainly the easiest to understand is that of geographical isolation. Imagine a population that has extended onto a peninsula, and after a great storm the peninsula becomes an island. If the plant or animal can neither swim nor fly, the population on the island and that on the mainland can no longer meet to interbreed. For each, because of their separate localities, there may soon be different selective pressures, and before long the genetic characters of the two populations may be so radically different that they are no longer capable of interbreeding, even if they are artificially crossed, and therefore by definition have become two separate species. There are many other possible geographic barriers, and it is, for instance, quite possible that a mountain range which separates two valleys is sufficient to keep the populations isolated.

Besides geographical isolation, other types have been postulated as well. There is some indication that two species may have arisen from one in the same locality. If, for instance, certain flies find both the treetops and the ground useful feeding and breeding places in a dense jungle, then it is quite possible that there may be ultimately no cross-mating between the upper and lower populations. This is again a spatial isolation, but in the same geographical region. It is even possible that the flies feed and breed in the same space, but those that are active at dawn never meet with those that are active at dusk; therefore they become isolated in time, and in this way may develop into two separate species. We could greatly extend the list, but let us simply conclude that the opportunities for species formation are numerous, and turn to the question of why they form.

It is not enough to say that if a population separates, the automatic result is two species. There is no reason why the selection pressures in both localities might not be sufficiently similar so that the two populations could be potentially interbreeding for great periods of time, even though they are never presented with the opportunity. A more positive way of looking at the problem comes if we return to the notion of niche and think of the opportunities available to a species. In crude terms, if one species has two opportunities, or slots, available to it, it will transform into two species. The reason that it will not remain one, occupying two positions, is that the different positions will exert different selection pressures. Furthermore, since the selection pressures are different, they can exploit their respective niches more efficiently by being different, and in order to maintain this difference, there will be selective pressures which will prevent crossbreeding so as not to dilute the new gains in being especially adapted to a new niche. Of course one must clearly recognize that this, as is characteristic of so much of thought about evolution, is pure conjecture. It is a reasonable explanation, but no more. It must always be remembered, in discussing evolution, that there is no way in which one can rerun a full-scale experiment over millions of years. Therefore our only approach is to gather as many facts as possible and try to find the most reasonable hypothesis. Even though we can see animals and plants, and possibly whole populations of them, we cannot span the time required for evolution. So in this sense evolutionary problems are still far too big for us to encompass, and it is for this reason that there will always remain some conjecture, some uncertainty. This will be so no matter how positively or dogmatically any particular position is put forward, and where there is some lack of certainty, human nature tends to become dogmatic.

To return to species formation, in our examples so far we have always talked of one species becoming two, but this was for the sake of simplicity; we could just as well have described one becoming three or more. The classic case of multiple species formation is that described by Darwin for the finches on the Galapagos Islands. These islands were presumably devoid of small birds until one species of finch appeared at some early period. These finches have turned into a variety of species, each one of which occupies a separate niche. There are finches that eat seeds, as indeed their ancestors must have; there are finches that eat insects, as do flycatchers; there are finches that poke out grubs from trees; as do woodpeckers. Furthermore each of these new species has structural changes that go with the new feeding habit. We surmise all these niches (and more as well, for we have oversimplified) were unoccupied on these isolated islands, and when the original finch species arrived they changed by selection into numerous new species accounting for all the niches available.

We have thus far treated populations as though they were simply numbers of individuals, but in recent years it has been appreciated that the populations themselves may have some structure as the result of the interaction among the individuals. This is especially obvious in animals, and one talks of animal societies, but to a modest degree it is even possible in immobile plants. The distribution of plants in any region is to a large extent determined by the physical environment; for example, alders will form along streams, grass in the meadows, and conifers on the mountain hillside. However, the plants themselves also play an important role in their own distribution. Not only do they do so by their method of seed dispersal and vegetative growth along the ground, but it is known that certain plants will produce inhibiting substances in the soil that will prevent competing plants from growing in their immediate vicinity. In this case plants form territories, which play such an important role in animal population, as we shall see presently.

The behavior of animals has been a most active area of research in recent years, and there are many who say that it remains one of the great unsolved problems and that it will be a central subject of investigation in the coming years. Behavior can, of course, be attacked from many levels: there are the outward interactions of the animals, which play a key role in social structure; there is the response of an individual to his surroundings; and there is the problem of how sensory and motor activities are processed by the brain and the rest of the nervous system. All three are related, but the last is considered to be the great frontier. We shall be concerned in this chapter with the first, for we are dealing with populations.

The behavior of animals in groups is an ancient subject, but because of a new school of animal behavior under natural conditions (called ethology), our understanding of these problems has vastly increased in recent years. We now have at least a skeleton picture of how bird and mammal societies are organized.

The first step in the relation of an animal with members of its own group is the relation between parent and offspring. Feeding and care require all sorts of mutual communication, and it has been shown that the offspring elicits automatic responses in the parent and the parent elicits automatic responses in the offspring. The jarring of a branch as the mother bird lands near the nest automatically stimulates the chick to open his mouth as wide as possible with a great display of throat, and this gape overwhelms the mother with a desire to cram a worm down the craw. All the parent-child relations are social ones even though they are confined within a family. There are a few interesting instances where this is not the case. For instance, penguins put all the chicks in one large communal group, or crèche, and take turns caring for this army of babies. Furthermore, the responses between parent and offspring are innate. A particular stimulus elicits a particular response, and the response is of such a nature that it fits in with our old concept of an instinct. Instincts are not only triggered into action by a particular cue from another individual, but the ability to respond is to a large extent conditioned by the internal physiology of the organism. In particular the hormones have a striking effect, and certain child-care urges will possess a mother full of lactating hormones. At some other times she does not give motherly responses to child stimuli.

The other primary social interactions between individuals are also connected with reproduction, and those are the mating reactions. Again they are conditioned by internal hormone activity (if the hormones are removed, no such activity occurs), and they depend upon a series of mutual stimuli and responses between the two courting partners. One of the interesting features in all of these cases

A Population 75

is that not only is there an alternating stimulus and response ritual between the individuals but the sequence is rigid and one step must follow the next in a specific order. This is even more surprising when one sees that the hormone changes also go through a set sequence, so that behavior and the internal physiology have a fixed pattern or cycle. From our point of view here, the important fact is that the individuals are brought together in close communication with one another, the key element of social grouping.

All higher animals are social to the extent we have discussed so far, but many have an even more social existence—for instance, animals which form herds, such as elk or certain other species of deer. These gatherings may be seasonal and connected with reproduction, or in some cases not. A good example of the latter is the fall gathering of starlings and grackles. Other animals, on the other hand, remain grouped permanently all year, such as baboon or howling monkey groups, or the colonies of rooks, to give an instance among birds.

The details of the organization of these different kinds of groupings are both remarkable and fascinating. One of the prime characteristics is that there is invariably within the group, no matter how closely or loosely knit, an order of dominance. This is often called the pecking order, for it was first described in chickens. A group of individuals has a rank, a hierarchy, and except for the individual at the top and the one at the bottom of the totem pole, each animal has some other animal who pushes him or her around and some other animal he or she can push around. To varying degrees this gives a definite structure to the society; in some cases, such as baboons, it appears harsh and autocratic, while in others, such as howling monkeys, the distinctions are mild and easy-going. One of the most striking results is the appearance of a true leader, who guides the movement of the group and is often the prime sentinel in the detection of danger.

Another important characteristic of these social groupings is their communication. It has become increasingly obvious in recent years that social birds and mammals have a considerable language. They make sounds and produce gestures that mean definite things to the rest of the group. The best known is, of course, the alarm note, and there is often more than one to give an indication of the degree of danger. Animal language has suddenly become a respectable subject after years of neglect, almost since the days of Saint Francis of Assisi.

So far we have talked about behavior patterns which tend to bring the population of animals together in groups, but there are equally important ones which tend to disperse the animals—primarily the process of territory formation, which is one of the most common phenomena among vertebrates. A bird, a fish, or a mammal will mark off a certain area and defend that area so as to exclude all other members of the same species. It is generally the male that does this territorial fighting, and he will either defend it for his nest site or defend it for the living and feeding area of his whole group, as is the case, for instance, with wolf packs, or howling monkey clans. The result is the formation of territories, which gives a spacing to the population that is to some extent rigid and controlled.

We have given evidence for grouping and ordered spacing in populations, but we cannot leave the matter here: biologists want to know, most of all, what is the reason for these patterns of behavior. If one accepts the concept of natural selection, then one assumes that these qualities have adaptive value, that is, are specifically culled and sifted out by natural selection. If this is the case, what advantages do they confer which permit social individuals to have more offspring than nonsocial ones? The assigning of adaptive superiority to any particular trait is one of the easiest indoor sports, for it is exceedingly difficult to prove or disprove any particular conjecture. The opportunities for the free roaming of the imagination are almost without limits, and the multitude of hypotheses leads to endless argument.

Having clearly marked the pitfalls, let us now jump in. The advantages of grouping might be numerous, and here are a few possibilities: Defense and protection against predators might be more effective in groups; alarm systems can certainly operate effectively and sheer numbers may intimidate the enemy; reproduction may be facilitated, for opposite sexes are brought together in numbers; and again, the young may be more protected in the group.

There are so many different kinds of grouping that these generalizations are somewhat inadequate, but this is the type of rationalization that is suggested.

One advantage of territoriality is usually considered to be the most efficient use of food resources. A territory is just large enough to maintain a family or a group. If the animals took less space, then they would starve. If this is correct, it means that the organisms have, by natural selection, produced a means of limiting the number of individuals, a fact which appears somewhat at variance with the idea that natural selection can be best considered in terms of reproductive success. It is not necessarily contradictory, however, because in order to have many individuals over many generations, a certain stability in numbers is required. Reproductive success does not mean simply more offspring, it means more children, grandchildren, and great-grandchildren—success in contributing to future generations. If the number of offspring vastly exceeds the food supply, famine and catastrophe may be the result. Territories provide stability in numbers with respect to resources, which is a most sophisticated way of insuring reproductive success. The stability gained by this steady state is directly responsible for the animal's evolutionary success.

One of the most pertinent questions of our time concerns human population. Our rate of increase at the moment is so staggering that one wonders if we have not lost, in all our glories of civilization, some basic biological control system. Certainly many primitive human societies do control their numbers, and it is clear that in solving our human population problems for the future we would do well to study the method of other animals.

As an epilogue to this discussion of populations, brief mention should be made of insect societies. These fantastic social structures of bees, ants, and termites never cease to stagger the imagination. Furthermore, there is every evidence that they have existed for millions of years in conditions of great stability.

The difference between insect societies and societies of higher organisms is that the former consist of one family, while the latter will be many families. As an example, many ants mate during a nuptial flight. The male dies and the new queen will begin laying eggs. She nurses the larvae until they emerge as adults. These eggs produce workers, which are sterile females, and as soon as they emerge from their cocoons they will help in the housekeeping and nursing of the succeeding broods. Soon many thousands of workers will build an elaborate nest, forage for food, care for the young, and protect the nest against invaders. Depending upon their nutrition during the larval stage, the workers may be small or large, or in some species produce soldiers with massive jaws. All these hordes of sexless amazons have one mother whom they protect and coddle in a fitting fashion. New colonies are produced by the manufacture of a reproductive brood, which flies off to mate and start new colonies elsewhere.

These huge families are exceedingly rigid in all their patterns. Many birds and mammals have a closely knit family structure, at least during some seasons, but it is very modest in size compared to a beehive or an ant nest. Having gone from a population to a family, we are now ready to take the next big step down, to that of an individual organism.

An Organism

6

MOST PLANTS AND ANIMALS ARE OF A SIZE WE CAN easily see. It is true that bacteria and other microorganisms may be very small, but with the help of a microscope they too can be observed. Furthermore, the rates of movement of organisms both large and small are such that they can be seen: they are not too rapid for the human eye. Even their life histories are within our comprehension. At the size level of living organisms, we are closest to our direct experience. This does not mean that all the problems have been solved. Quite the opposite is the case, for it sometimes seems to be that the more easily we can see a problem, the more difficult and complex it is.

Let us begin by placing living organisms in a size scale. The smallest will be bacteria, a few microns in length, and the largest will be giant sequoias, some 360 feet high, or blue whales, some 100 feet long. If one compares the characteristics of different-sized organisms, one of the most obvious facts is that the larger the organism, the longer it takes to grow to maturity. The easiest measure of growth is the time taken from the beginning of growth to the moment the organism is sufficiently mature to be able to reproduce itself. This so-called generation time is a more consistent measure than life span, or the time that an organism survives before it dies; life span seems to vary greatly and show only a rough correlation with size. Generation time, on the other hand, is directly related to size, and the larger the organism the longer it takes to reach reproductive maturity. The extremes will be bacteria, which are a few microns long and divide every half hour or so, at one end of the scale; and at the other end, giant sequoias, which begin producing cones when they reach a height of some 260 feet, a size they attain only after 60 years of growth; all other animals and plants fall somewhere in between.

The reason for this correlation is obvious. Since each generation is mainly a period of growth, a period of construction, it simply takes longer to build something large than something small. This is obvious enough in the building trade, for it takes longer to build a sky-scraper than a one-room shack; there are simply more operations, more steps that are required. The very same argument applies to the building of mature organisms.

One rather puzzling question is why is it necessary to do so much building. There are two parts to this question, and one is why are there large organisms at all. One always hears that nature is efficient, even parsimonious, and never does anything in vain. Why therefore do we find any animal or plant larger than a bacterium? As with all such questions the biologist immediately falls back on the notion of natural selection. He argues that for some reason there must have been adaptive advantages to being larger and therefore selective pressure for size increase. Nothing could be easier to rationalize; for instance, a larger organism can more effectively chase and eat a smaller one. Or in the case of a plant, a larger one can reach above a smaller one and take first chance at the sun's rays for photosynthesis. The hypotheses can be greatly multiplied, but perhaps it is easier to say simply that larger and larger organisms have appeared during the course of geological time. This is an evolutionary fact, evident from

An Organism

AN individual elk; a mature male with fine antlers.

82 *The Scale of Nature*

the fossil record, and there are many ways in which we can suggest explanations as to why this is the case.

There is another interesting correlation with size. The larger the organism, the more complex. This is also a very general principle and applies to buildings as well as living constructions. Again the reason for it is obvious, for with increased size there are increased problems of servicing the organism so that it can operate properly. To give a simple example, if an organism is small it can get oxygen directly from the environment by diffusion. But if it is large, it is too thick for the oxygen to diffuse inward. Therefore, in order that combustion can take place at all in a large animal, there must be lungs or gills for gas exchange and a circulatory system to carry the oxygen inside the body. These structures are highly elaborate and a direct result of the size of the animal. The cost of increased size is considerable in terms of complexity and division of labor.

The other part of the question of why there is so much large building going on is more subtle. In bacteria and other unicellular organisms, the cell divides in half and each half grows until it reaches a mature size again ready for the next division. This involves some construction, but a relatively simple one in which only half the organism is regenerated. Large trees and mammals, or for that matter any reasonable-sized animals or plants, do not split in half but do something far more radical. They give off single cells in the form of egg or sperm which, following fertilization, grow into huge sequoias or whales. They start from scratch, from a single cell, and build a large and complex structure each generation. Again the harder road seems to have been followed and again we ask for the reason.

Why is it necessary to start from one cell? One answer might be that it is easier to build from the beginning than make half a tree or half a mammal. This, however, is a very doubtful argument and I would not like to have to defend it. A better answer comes from the genetic system and the importance of recombination which we have already mentioned. The genes from the parents are carried on the chromosomes, one set from the father and one from the mother. These are brought together by fertilization, a process which can be accomplished only by single cells. This is a requirement of the method of inheritance which is bound up in the nucleus. Each fertilized egg can vary depending upon how the genes are combined, but it is possible to make this kind of arrangement only with single cells. To make the point clear, if an elephant split lengthways in two, both halves would be the same, and would not offer the kind of variation necessary for natural selection to take place. In bacteria this is no problem because they are always single cells, and they vary primarily by mutation. That is, if one cell possesses a gene which has altered by mutation, it can pass it on directly to its offspring. The reason, then, that large organisms begin their existence as single cells has to do with their mechanism of inheritance and variation, the prime requisites of natural selection. Therefore it is not surprising that the single-cell stage has been retained, even in the case of the gigantic plants and animals. In fact, it would be fair to say that these larger animals never could have evolved unless they had remained minute single cells at one stage in their life history.

The discussion so far serves to emphasize a basic point about organisms. We tend by natural habit on our part to think of organisms as adults, but yet we know perfectly well that an organism is an organism at all stages of its life history, from the fertilized egg through the embryo, and all the stages of immaturity, the reproducing adult, and even the senile and decrepit individual. Therefore in this sense it is more realistic to think of organisms as life cycles rather than individuals at one instant in time. If they are considered life cycles, then, to repeat what we have said before, in these new terms, organisms that become large adults have long life cycles. We can now go one step further and study the life cycle in terms of size periods. After fertilization we have an extended period of size increase, which is commonly called development. This is followed by a period of maturity, where the size may remain the same. During this latter period of size equilibrium, there may be a cutting off of new reproductive cells, usually in the form of egg or sperm, and this liberation of gametes is a period of abrupt size decrease.

In the case of the life cycle, we have already discussed at least some aspects of why, from an evolutionary point of view, there are periods of size change, and now we come to some of the burning questions of modern biology. How are these changes made—how does a single cell grow into a whale or a tree? What are the rules that make this construction sufficiently precise so that it is consistent from generation to generation?

It is known that a great many of the messages, the instructions which govern development, come from the genes in the nucleus. In single-celled organisms these are carried out directly in the cytoplasm, the living substance immediately surrounding the nucleus. There is considerable evidence that there is a set sequence of events which consists of a series of reactions that affect alternately the nucleus and the cytoplasm. Gene products enter the cytoplasm, which is modified and in turn affects the nucleus, so that a new gene is activated, which in turn makes new products. As we shall see when we enter into the size level of large or macromolecules, the biochemist has been very busy trying to identify these substances and analyze these steps on a biochemical level.

Before proceeding further, it is important to consider what kind of information is passed on, what kind of events occur in development. They can be classified in a number of ways, and a convenient way to think of them is as three constructive processes: *growth, morphogenetic movement,* and *differentiation*. By growth is meant synthesis of new protoplasm; this is accompanied by cell and nuclear division in multicellular organisms. Development of a tree is a common example of growth. Morphogenetic movements are found primarily in developing animals where the cells move and produce a new shape. The best-known such movement is that of gastrulation, where an embryo folds upon itself to become multilayered. In the process of differentiation, different parts of an organism take on different compositions and structures. This is really equivalent to division of labor, for these different parts are associated with different functions. As an example, cells in some parts of one body are muscle, some nerve, and some cartilage, and these different cell types are organized in well-formed organs and tissues which divide the labor.

One of the problems the developmental biologist wishes to solve is the nature of these three processes themselves, even without considering their overall role in development. In the case of growth, this has turned out to be primarily a problem of chemical synthesis, and many of the biochemical pathways are known. The mechanism of morphogenetic movement is far less understood, largely because the mechanism of amoeboid motion (which is the way the embryonic cells move) is not known. Many kinds of differentiation are also being studied by the biochemist, who seeks to follow the chemical reactions which lead to the altered structure.

There is another set of problems, at a higher level, and at the heart of developmental biology. We want to know how these three processes—growth, morphogenetic movement, and differentiation—are controlled so that the end result is the perfect and constant form of the adult. If growth is not held in check, then some parts will grow way out of proportion to others; that is precisely what appears to occur in the growth of cancers. If morphogenetic movement is not carefully guided, the result is formless chaos. If differentiation is not controlled, all the delicate balance of proportions between the different cell and tissue types, as well as their proper positioning in space, is lost. Therefore we not only want to know how each process occurs, but we want to know the master plan of how it is controlled so that the processes all come out to perfection.

We think of each of the processes of development as producing an internal condition which inevitably leads to the next stage. It is like a series of steps in a set sequence in which the end result is the inevitable result, given the initial reactants and their initial organization. This is not a new idea; it goes back at least to Aristotle. The question now is how can we solve the riddle of this sequence of steps so that we feel we understand this difficult problem of biology.

The approach today is to come back to consider the reactants in terms of gene products and changing cytoplasmic environments. We have already mentioned this in discussing unicellular organisms, but the problem becomes more complex in multicellular ones. Here a nucleus divides repeatedly (by mitosis), so that each cell apparently contains the complete genetic complement of the organism. The question is how is it possible, in this population of identical nuclei, to obtain differences in parts, that is, differentiation?

If the cells are firmly stuck to one another, as they are in plants with rigid cell walls, then somehow different regions of the organism will be different in some way. This differentiation may be due to the environment of the cell: some parts, for instance, may be more exposed and therefore have greater gas exchange than others, or more radiation. Environment may affect the cytoplasm of those regions, which in turn affects the nuclei, so that nuclei in different parts of the organism are receiving different signals from the cytoplasm. There are also internal ways in which differences in parts may arise. One of the most interesting yet puzzling ways is by the polar movement of substances. In the case of higher plants, hormones, produced by the cells, will move in one direction more than in another. The result is an accumulation of the substance at one end of the organism, again causing a differential stimulus on the nuclei at that end.

If the cells are mobile and can undergo morphogenetic movement, they can, by their movement, enter areas which differ in chemical environment, thereby producing the necessary stimuli to begin the events that lead to differentiation. In animals there is usually a combination of growth and morphogenetic movement which, with the help of polar movement of substances and other spacing behavior, produce the desired and consistent adult shape.

The developmental biologist seeks to understand all these steps so that he can explain the wonderful process of how a fertilized egg turns into a tree or an animal. The difficulty has been that there are so many steps that, if they are considered in terms of chemical reactions, to catalogue them all would be well nigh impossible. The biologist has, therefore, attempted to find those steps which are particularly significant in the developmental process. The progress has been slow, but the hope for the future is great. In the meantime there has been some impatience, for genetics has made great strides forward and developmental biology has shown no such flowering. "Nature keeps some of her secrets longer than others."

Before considering the adult organism, let us briefly mention the period of size decrease, that is, primarily, the period of the production of reproductive cells, where the organism cuts off small bodies such as spores or egg and sperm. Multicellular animals and plants are characterized by being a collection of cells which firmly adhere to one another. The only point where they become unstuck is when they produce reproductive cells that are scattered to begin the next generation. It has been suggested that life cycles of multicellular forms might be considered an alternation of adhesive and non-adhesive states; the former being the state of the developing and maturing organism, and the latter being gamete or spore formation. It is certainly true that one of the most significant changes in gamete formation is the loss of adhesion. But there are other important events also, such as the construction of the motile sperm and the storage of yolk in the developing egg, and all the hormonal changes that go on within the body that lead to gamete production. These processes are also thought to involve a series of chemical events, one of which follows another in a set sequence. The kind of event, then, that occurs in development—namely, the sequence of steps—occurs in other stages of the life cycle as well; it is characteristic of life cycles and not just the period of development.

The main period of size equilibrium is that of the adult, and in considering the functioning of the adult we enter into the older domains of physiology and anatomy. These disciplines have flourished for a long period of time, and as we shall see, there are certain aspects of physiology that still retain the greatest interest in modern research.

Let us begin with plant anatomy and physiology, for two reasons: plants are far simpler than animals, but even more important, most plants do not have a mature stage that corresponds with anything we find among animals. Large trees (as well as many smaller plants) keep growing; they never cease their period of size increase. The botanist refers to this property as continuing embryology. It means that the growth zones at the apex of the plant and at the apices of all the shoot and root branches keep growing, as well as the cambium, which is responsible for the thickening of the branches and the trunk of the tree. If the tree seems to have a size limit, it is only that eventually, as a result of age and decay, the wind will fell it. Other plants, such as annual plants, do reach a growth limit, but in this case all the cells, except for those of the seed, die. As a hayfield turns brown or a wheat field turns to light gold, the cells of the plant wither and dry, leaving a dead stalk to hold the seed so it may scatter in the winds.

Yet even though plants do not have an adult stage that corresponds to that of animals, they certainly have an anatomy and a physiology. But plant physiology is largely, for the very reasons we have given, the physiology of development. The concern is with growth hormones, oriented growth movements with respect to light and gravity, and related problems, all of which are completely within the outlook of the developmental biologist. Plants have no nervous system, no muscles, no means of locomotion comparable to that of animals. For simplicity's sake I am confining my remarks to higher animals and plants, for indeed in more primitive forms the distinction between the two is rather fuzzy. Furthermore, among higher plants there are a few exceptions, such as the sensitive plant which drops its leaf suddenly at a touch, and certain fly-catching plants that have relatively rapid movements. But these are physiological curiosities and hardly in the main line of significant problems in biology.

If we turn to animals, some aspects of adult physiology hold pressing problems for the future. In considering these we are again confronted with the matter of the size level. The physiological activities can be considered at the level of the entire organism, the organ, the tissue, the cells, and even the biochemical events which take place within the cells.

Let us briefly consider these functions from the point of view of the animal organism. To begin, the assimilation of energy in the form of food is a prime essential. It involves claw, beak, or teeth along with a mouth to begin the food processing and then an alimentary canal to digest the food and absorb it into the blood and thence move it to the tissues. Another function is locomotion. The whole animal can swim or fly or run, and this involves the contraction of muscle situated in key positions and properly coordinated. The animal must not only govern the eating and digestive processes but also move; at all moments it must make the appropriate responses to its changing environment.

Of these three primary physiological activities which are characteristic of living organisms (*energy assimilation, locomotion,* and *coordination*) , the first two are fairly well understood, at least in their broad outline. This is especially true of assimilation. In the case of movement, there remain some outstanding questions, especially on the biochemical and cellular level, where the problem of the molecular basis of muscle contraction is being sought. There has, however, been much exciting progress made along these lines in recent years.

There is one pertinent point concerning size and the movement of animals that should be mentioned. The larger the animal the faster it can move, if we consider the fastest animal for any particular size level. This relation is rough but it holds from the smallest unicellular animal to the large multicellular ones up to about 10 feet in length. Whales and elephants do not have great speed. Furthermore, it holds for animals that swim, run, and fly. A tuna fish will rush along at 2,080 centimeters per second, which is about 47 miles per hour, while a motile bacterium will only move at the rate of 1.5×10^{-3} centimeter per second.

Of all the aspects of physiology, in many ways the most intriguing, the most complex, and therefore the least well understood is the problem of coordination. This is the essence of the problem of control. We have already discussed coordination among individual animals in an animal society; here we are concerned with the coordination among cells and tissues within one organism. We have stepped down onto a smaller size level.

From the point of view of the level of the organism, each animal is a beautifully functional whole. His internal organs and digestive processes are under overall nervous control, his locomotion is steered by nerve activity; in fact the very properties which characterize an individual animal and his actions, his oneness, are all to be found in the functioning of the nervous system. Therefore we see that the nervous system not only governs the animal's social activities but his bodily activities as well. In order to analyze this internal coordination further, we will descend the size scale and examine the organs of an animal. We will go from whole organisms to parts of organisms, and while we will discuss organs in general of plants and animals, we will lay special stress on the nervous system.

Organs

7

PLANTS HAVE ORGANS, BUT THEY ARE EXTREMELY
simple when compared to those of animals. The leaf, the root,
the fruit, and so forth may each be considered an organ. They are
the result of the process of differentiation and carry out specific activities in the division of labor. For instance, the leaf catches the sunlight
and is the organ of photosynthesis; the root assimilates water and salt
from the soil as well as anchoring the plant in position; the fruit is
a structure which holds the seed and facilitates its dispersal. The
list could, of course, be easily extended, but the principle is clear.

What is less clear is why the organs of plants are simpler than those
of animals. The answer is probably to be found in the fact that plants
are photosynthetic and nonmotile (again, for simplicity, we are only
talking of the extreme case of higher plants) . Even the fact that they
are nonmotile is related to the fact that they are photosynthetic.
There is no reason to move in photosynthesis, except perhaps to keep
the leaf at right angles to the sun for maximum absorption, and this

An Organ

THE organ shown here is the eye of an elk. The cutaway hole in the back is to show the retinal layer, which records the image thrown onto its surface by the lens.

The Scale of Nature

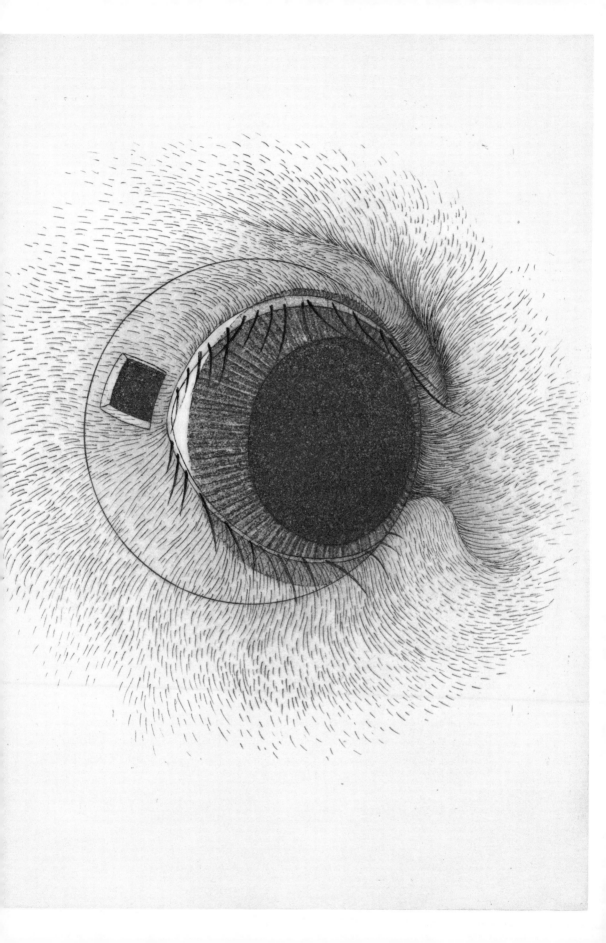

is achieved by slow movements which follow the sun through its course in the sky. But this slight movement is achieved by the simple procedure of altering the water content, or turgor pressure, of the cells on the two sides of the plant, and the same principle is true in a more rapid form, in the closing of the trap in Venus's flytrap. If a plant need not move to chase its food, its requirements of oxygen and energy for respiration are less; running a hundred-yard dash is an expensive process in terms of fuel combustion. If the respiration rate is low, then the need in large plants for a circulatory system with a heart pump and a breathing system is absent. The digestive system is not needed because of photosynthesis. The only requirement left with respect to food is to have channels for the movement of water, salts, and sugars so that all the parts of the plants can live and obtain what they lack from other parts. So plants have a food-transportation system, or vascular system, in the wood (xylem) and bast (phloem), which does everything in the way of food circulation that is necessary, but it does not concern itself with rapid gas exchange, which is so necessary for active animals. Finally, plants need not have a finely coordinated nervous system for there are no movements, no reactions to sudden changes, which require such elaborate control. The only thing animals and plants have in common is some kind of supporting system, but again that of animals is articulated and connected by muscles and tendons, while that of plants is rigid and inflexible.

Animals, by contrast, are replete with complex organs. There are many organs connected with the digestive system (for example, mouth, esophagus, stomach, pancreas), with the circulatory system (for example, heart, spleen), with the excretory system, and with the reproductive system. We cannot here attempt to describe them all, but we will concentrate on those connected with the control of the animal organism, for invariably the matter of control is one which has the greatest attraction and fascination.

The nervous system is organized in such a fashion that there is a central brain, a nerve cord connected to the brain, and nerve fibers which branch out to various regions of the body including all the sense organs. These sense organs specialize in particular external stimuli: chemical receivers for smell and taste, radiation receivers for sight, sound-vibration receivers for hearing, pressure receivers, temperature receivers, and pain receivers. With all these outposts the body is able to gather all sorts of information, and it will often convert this information into action, or motor activity, as it is called. The body runs away from a frightening noise, or it rushes toward food which it sees and smells. The information is recorded in the sense organs, where it passes to the brain and the central nervous system along the sensory nerves. In the central nervous system the information is converted into action and passed out on the motor nerves to the specific muscles for a specific action. This is the overall pattern of animal coordination. And now comes the question of how it works.

Here we are considering the matter at the level of the organ; let us first discuss different sense organs. Anatomically the most elaborate, and the one which we value more than any other, is the eye. It has a lens which focuses an image on the retina, the surface of which is lined with photoreceptor cells. These cells (rods and cones) contain a photosensitive pigment which is altered by light. It has been shown that if one killed a rabbit which had been staring at a pattern of light and dark, the exact image could be seen on the retina itself by the bleaching of the photosensitive pigment in certain areas; it was precisely like developing a film from a camera.

The rods and cones have a direct nerve connection to the brain, and in fact bring this information to a specific region of the brain. That the pattern is fixed has been shown in newts, which have quite fantastic powers of regeneration. If the eye is removed and replaced in an inverted position (180-degree shift), the fibers regenerate from the eye back to the brain, and by some utterly remarkable and incomprehensible process, each fiber rejoins with its old connection in the brain. After this has been accomplished, the newt sees upside down; if some food is put above him he reaches ineffectively downward for it.

The eye is sensitive to exceedingly small quantities of light; it is highly efficient as a light detector. The ear, at least in some organisms, is equally effective in detecting small amounts of noise. The vibrations of sound are sensed by small hairs in the snaillike cochlea of the ear, and each of these hairs has a nerve connection to the brain. The beauty of this mechanism has been brought home by the studies of the bat echo location. It has been shown that the bat emits high-pitched sounds and that it is sufficiently sensitive to these sounds to be able to hear them as they bounce off objects. The system is so delicate that a blinded bat can catch a small insect as it flies through the air (or catch a grub thrown by the experimenter).

The speed and the precision of these actions are so far beyond human capacities that they are hard to imagine. The fact that radar systems use principles somewhat similar to bat echo location has helped our comprehension, but we are faced with a good example of something experienced in our own size range (in this instance, bats) which we had not expected simply because it is not one of our own capabilities. The closest we come to it is a practice of the pilots of boats. I can remember going through the San Juan Islands in Puget Sound in a fog. The channel between the islands is very narrow, yet it was impossible to see either shore. The ferryboat pilot first politely told all the mothers to ask their children to stop their ears. Then he blasted his horn while he leaned out the pilothouse on one side, and repeated the operation as he leaned out the other side. By judging the time it took for the echo to return, he could gauge his distance from the shore. He seemed far more composed about the process than I.

But the catching of a small insect going by at considerable speed is a different, almost inconceivable, proposition. It tells us again how our knowledge is limited by what we can see, hear, or smell. One wonders how many things are going on about us of which we are unaware, either because we have no sense organ to record them, or because what sense organ we do have is in some way inadequate. For instance, we are insensitive to radio waves, and this obviously explains why it was so late in our civilization before their existence was discovered. How many other manifestations exist about us of which we are ignorant? Perhaps some lesser animal is not only aware but makes important use of them.

To some extent this is the case with the sense of smell. We know that our best friend, the dog, has a remarkably good nose and demonstrates his skill to us daily. Consider the bloodhound tracking a criminal for miles solely on the basis of a whiff of one of his articles of clothing. How does the man's smell get to the bottom of his rubber shoes to leave behind a track? It has been shown that a dog need not follow such a track only through wilderness, where no other man has passed, but he can do it through city streets, across the tracks of countless other persons.

Much work has been done on insects, who also show amazing sensitivity to minute amounts of chemicals. Male moths, as was shown in the old experiments of Henri Fabre, will go miles to find females. The scent is wafted through the evening air, and even though diluted to the point where only a few molecules will reach the delicate chemical sense organs on the antennae, the male, upon receiving the stimulus, will begin flying upwind, coming closer and closer to his prospective mate. The nearest that human beings come to such feats is wine tasting or perfume smelling. The French, with their wonderful gift for cooking, have cultivated the nose and the taste buds to the extent that not only can they detect the vineyard of the wine, but the year as well. This may not seem to be a very useful skill to some, but to others it is almost a matter of life and death.

Besides having sight, hearing, and chemical senses, animals are also sensitive to pressure. The process here is thought to be akin to the recording of sounds, since sound waves are disturbances in pressure. The pressure-sensitive receptor that most closely resembles an ear in its mechanism is the one giving position and balance of the animal (with respect to gravity). In its simplest form it consists of a cavity which contains a stone or a small hard object. The cavity is lined with sensitive hairs, and by this means the position of the stone in the cavity, which is affected by gravity, is recorded in the brain by direct nerve connection, and the animal knows if it is right side up or on its side. There are also pressure receptors all over one's body, which record any kind of push or pinch. These are simple affairs especially designed to give off signals if they are squeezed.

Temperature receptors are less well understood. They exist all over the surface of our bodies and some record warmth and some coldness. Equally puzzling are the pain receptors, which appear as the simplest sort of nerve endings, but which, if damaged, produce the most frightful sensations of internal agony. That these three kinds of receptors are useful to the organism for avoidance of danger and the seeking of a tolerable environment is self-evident.

Thus far we have discussed the input, the receivers from the outside world; next let us look briefly at the output, or the motor system. The motor nerves leave the central nervous system and go directly to the muscles. It is one of the oldest experiments in elementary physiology to remove the calf muscle from the leg of a frog along with its attached nerve, and stimulate the nerve with an electric shock in order to produce a contraction of the muscle. All the muscles of the body have their nerve connections. Many of them we can cause to contract by willing ourselves to do so, but there are others which contract without regard for our wishes. Those of the intestine are an example of the latter, and they possess a slightly different kind of muscle, which is appropriately called involuntary muscle. Hunger pains, butterflies in the stomach, and various intestinal activities carry on as though we did not exist. This automatic action is not significant so much in terms of the outgoing nerve and muscle as it is in terms of the central control in the spinal cord and in the brain.

If an action occurs without our conscious control, it is simply because the input and the output came to a center in the central nervous system below the cerebrum, below the region where we have consciousness. The input and the output carry on without our knowledge or our will to interfere. There is a slightly different situation, one made famous by Pavlov, where we are conscious of the input, but have no control over the output. This is the conditioned reflex, of which the classic example is salivation. If we see or sometimes even think of a juicy, sour lemon, we salivate whether we wish to or not; the action is entirely outside of our control. In this case we automatically associate salivating with lemons, and the connection of the pathway in the brain has been built up by the previous experience of sucking lemons. This shows among other things that the nervous system is capable of memory, and that at least this kind of memory apparently involves the creating of a nerve pathway that remains open and in fact is used at the sight of a lemon.

The greatest interest of all attaches to the higher centers of the brain. It has been shown, in great detail, that certain areas of the brain specialize in receiving information from specific sense organs, and other areas specialize in sending out conscious motor actions to the muscles. Not only is it possible to locate areas which correspond to different areas of skin (comprising the touch, temperature, and pain sense organs), but there are also special regions which receive information from the eye, the ear, and the taste-smell organs. Furthermore, within the visual area, the different parts of the retina which contain the cells with the visual pigment are directly connected to discrete parts of the brain, so that the visual field is laid out in the brain. This helps us to understand why, in the regenerative eye of the newt, when severed nerves are reconnected, the pattern remains inverted if the eye is inverted; the retina-brain pattern is fixed.

Besides the processing of sensory information and the converting of it into action, there are many other aspects of the brain that have received attention from both the physiologist and the psychologist. In particular the study of the process of learning has held a great interest. Years ago it was shown by Karl Lashley that if part of the brain of a rat was removed, the rat lost some of its ability to learn, and the amount of brain removed corresponded to the loss of learning capacity. The extraordinary thing was that in the case of learning, the part of the brain removed was not so important as the amount of tissue. This seems to differ from the previous information that parts of the brain correspond to specific sensory and motor systems. Apparently learning is a generalized activity, and the recording and acting upon sensory information is a strictly localized one. It is known, however, in cases of brain damage, especially at an early age, that the loss of a specific sense-receiving area can be functionally replaced by other neighboring areas. For instance, often as a result of a brain operation, the speech center of the brain may be removed or damaged. But after a period of recovery and training, it may be possible even for an adult to speak again in a normal fashion.

Thus we think of the brain as something which is to varying degrees pliable. We must wait until we begin talking of the brain as a tissue before we can seriously examine the anatomical basis of this pliability. Note that in contemplating the analysis of the brain in terms of its tissue construction, we are adopting a reductionist approach, but we have learned the nature of the problems from a consideration of the whole organism. There is no other way to define or even imagine the existence of such a process of learning.

Another similar process that is a property of the whole organ (and hopefully related to learning) is memory. Memory has many properties: there is both conscious and unconscious memory. By unconscious memory one might simply mean a conditioned reflex, but there is also a more sophisticated kind where, for instance, we cannot remember a name but it suddenly comes in a flash when we are thinking of something else. This brings us to the realm of psychology and the exploration of the conscious and subconscious.

There is no doubt that one of the more exciting occupations for an intelligent person is to read the remarkable writings of Sigmund Freud and various others such as Carl Gustav Jung. From a scientific point of view, their approach to the workings of the mind has met with much criticism because it is often impossible to subject the hypothesis to the minimum kinds of test for verification. This was especially true in the beginning, and perhaps the thrill of reading Freud is that his explanation is so outrageous, so bold, so imaginative, and yet so reasonable, that even if it may not be true one is certainly convinced that it is a beautiful idea. The genius transcends sordid notions of proof and disproof. An excellent example is Freud's views on errors; that small slips reveal the unconscious, what we are suppressing. This is indeed a hard thing to verify, but the brilliant suggestion seems to have so much on its side that it is hard to imagine anyone not convinced that there is something to the notion, even though it does not lend itself to any kind of a statistical analysis. Because of the uncertainty of many of the basic notions, Jung and many others have suggested alternate hypotheses, some of which are equally or sometimes more attractive as possible explanations of the activities of the human mind. The result often leads to polemics and the foundation of schools of psychology, a tendency that would not be so strong if the nature of the subject lent itself more effectively to convincing experiment. The fact that it does not should never for a moment lead one to think that it is a less important subject, which is a somewhat natural tendency for scientists in fields where exact measurements are possible. Even physiological psychologists, who study the senses and the nervous system, look with some distrust at the study of the mind. It is a subject that used to be part of philosophy, and to this day many psychologists are trained as philosophers. Words have meaning as do equations, but they also have meaning in terms of the activities of the human mind. Perhaps the time has come for some aspects of psychology to join up again with philosophy, for certainly the whole superstructure of science, that completely human enterprise, rests upon the activities of the mind. Furthermore, it is a subject, unlike the ones which we will pursue in the following pages, which has not found any way of being examined or understood in the analysis of its elements. It has utterly defied so far the reductionist approach and remains holistic and organismal. This has been a further cause for disagreement among scientists and for a misunderstanding of the study of psychology of whole animals.

We have finished this chapter with a discussion of the ultimate organ, the brain, and now we are prepared again to step down the size scale. We want to look at the tissues which make up the organs.

Tissues

8

WE SHALL NOW ATTEMPT TO SHOW HOW ORGANS and whole organisms may be interpreted in terms of their fine structure. The main example will be nervous activity and brain function in animals in terms of the activities of nerve tissues; but before we follow that thread, let us examine tissues in general.

Tissues are an association of cells and are therefore part of all multicellular organisms. Since multicellular organisms are characterized by differentiation, or division of labor, a tissue is an assembly of cells such as muscle or cartilage. These tissues may be brought together in organs, which are then part of a whole organism; they are this size level above the unit cells.

In higher plants, where the organs are simple compared to those of animals, the tissues are also uncomplicated. There is the wood, or xylem, and the bast, or phloem (the sieve tissue), to mention two. Each of these is made up of two types of cells: supporting fibers and conducting cells, which form the vascular system of the tree. One of the especially interesting features of the xylem is the fact that it soon dies and performs its supporting function as well as its function of transporting water and dissolved salt in this dead state. It is only the cells lying adjacent to the active growth zone, or cambium, that are still alive. One of the commonest tissues in higher plants (called parenchyma) is made up of live rectangular cells that are quite undifferentiated and wholly unspecialized; it is almost as though the tissue were a space filler of regions which have no specialized activities.

The main characteristic of plant tissues, and their basic difference from animal tissues, is that their constituent cells are covered with rigid cellulose walls and adhere firmly one to another. This basic bricklike feature of their architecture imposes all sorts of requirements upon them, many of which do not confront animal cells, which are soft-walled and mobile. The main restrictions are to be found in their mode of development, for plants are incapable of cellular movements, as we have already discussed.

One of the most interesting aspects of tissues is the interaction between cells. In most cases this involves a passing of substances from one cell or group of cells to another cell or group within the tissue. In animal tissues, where the cells are separated by extremely thin membranes, there is evidence that large molecules such as proteins can pass from one cell to the next. It is necessary, in these cases, for the cells to be in contact with one another. In plants the cellulose cell walls are so thick that it is impossible to pass large molecules from cell to cell; only the smallest can get through. It is not surprising, therefore, that the known plant hormones, which have been studied with such interest and intensity by the plant physiologist, consist of small molecules.

The study of these hormones remains one of the most important aspects of botany today. There are three sorts of questions that are being actively examined to explain the tissue interactions which are primarily responsible for the control of plant growth. The first is what tissue produces the hormone and how it is synthesized, and second is how it is transported to the tissue it will affect, and the

A Tissue

THE retinal layer is a complex tissue specialized to record light. At the top of the figure one can see a layer of rods and cones, the cells which actually receive the light. These are connected by a series of nerve cells and complex connections, which ultimately lead off (as shown in the lower portion of the plate) to the optic nerve and then on to the brain. It is surprising that the light must go through this layer of nerve cells in order to reach the sensitive rods and cones, yet clearly this does not keep the eye from being an extraordinarily sensitive and efficient instrument. The thickness of the tissue shown here is 250 microns (0.25 millimeters).

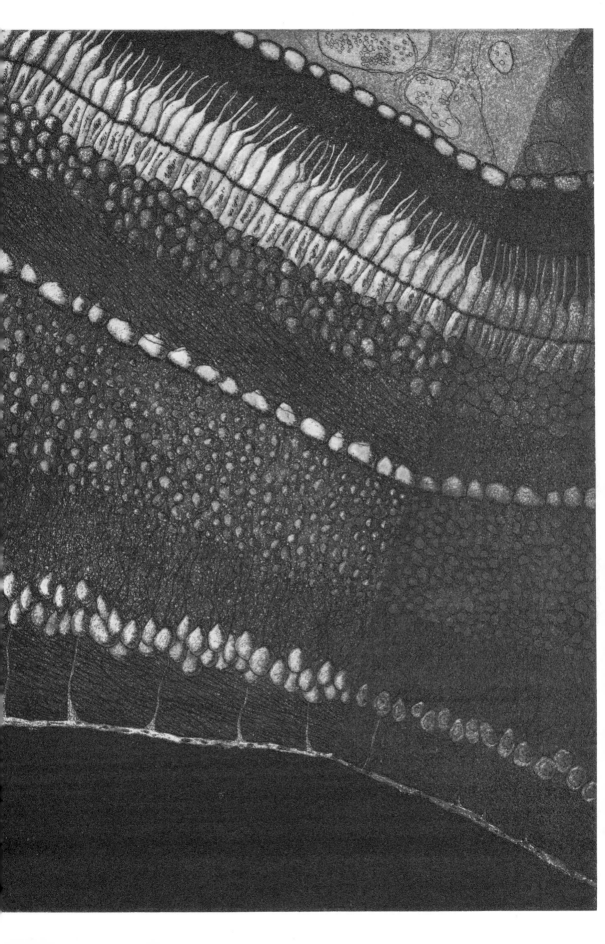

third is how it exerts its effect upon the tissue, whatever the effect may be (for example, stimulation of growth, inhibition of growth, flowering). It is quite obvious from what has been said here that the prime problems are being analyzed on the molecular size level, but this is only partially true. All the great advances so far in the physiology of plant hormones have been made on the tissue level: the discovery of the hormones themselves, the development of quantitative tests for the hormones, and the studies of the effects of the hormones upon plants. While this work must continue to forge the way and show what needs to be elucidated, there is no doubt that the molecular approach to these problems will have increasing significance and importance.

As an example, consider the current status of the second problem mentioned above, namely, the method of the transport of hormones from one area to another. It has been known for some years that in the shoot the growth hormone auxin moves primarily toward the root, and there is little or no movement in the reverse direction. This fact has great significance as far as the growth and form of the plant is concerned, and therefore we want to understand the mechanism. Thus far it has defied any satisfactory explanation; we only know that this polar movement far exceeds the rate expected from diffusion. Recently it has been possible to tag auxin with a radioactive carbon atom, apply this tagged auxin to different parts of the plants, and obtain very quick and accurate information as to its progress within the plant. With this new technique it is now possible to show that the auxin is only transported in live tissues; it will not show such movement in dead xylem. Also, it has been possible to study the process in the root (where the movement is directional, or polar, toward the shoot) and also study the movement in developing plants to demonstrate the point where this polar transport appears. Finally there has been some very recent work showing the effects of other substances on this polar movement of auxin. These studies have not yet solved the final problem of the basic mechanism of this directional movement, but no doubt they ultimately will do so. Then we shall have an understanding of one of the most important aspects of tissue interaction in plants, which may well have implications of significance for the understanding of all organisms.

Animal tissues are so varied that were we to try to describe them all, we would end with a stultifying list. Besides muscle and cartilage, there is bone, nervous tissue, tendon, connective tissue, and then the specialized tissues of different organs such as kidney, liver, spleen, and all the various glands. Again, here let us stress tissue interaction, for this is the subject which is of prime interest to the biologist today.

One of the most important kinds of tissue interaction is found in developing embryos. There is first of all the process of induction, in which one part of an embryo persuades other parts to develop and differentiate in a certain fashion. In the classic beginning of this study, Hans Spemann showed that a certain region of the developing embryo was capable of persuading the tissues lying adjacent to it to develop into the main axis of the embryo. It was assumed fairly early in these studies that this key region was producing some substance that was in some way capable of stimulating the surrounding tissues, and in the 1930's a great search began for the chemical identification of this substance. We still do not know what it is today (although we have learned very much in the process), but again there is a strong desire to put this problem on a molecular basis. The difficulty has been that any experimental procedure which damages the tissues results in those tissues giving off the stimulating substance. Therefore in any one experiment it is impossible to know if one's success in obtaining an induction is due to the test substance or to the damage and the release of some local substance.

Normally, in the developing animal, certain amoebalike cells called mesenchyme are responsible for persuading, or inducing, the embryonic kidney cells to turn into kidney tubules. It is possible to show this in tissue culture by mixing the two cell types; but the embryonic kidney cells alone will not differentiate. To analyze the factor responsible for this induction, each cell type was put on the opposite side of a membrane containing small holes, or pores. If the holes were small, then no induction took place, but if the holes were large enough so that masses of large molecules (such as strands of protein) were permitted to pass from one side to the other, then kidney tubules formed on the side opposite the mesenchyme. In this case the inductor seems to consist of some large complex of molecules. It is presumed that in different induction processes in different parts of the embryo, different substances are involved, although whether this is the case, what the substances are, and how they act remain key questions for the future.

These are not the only type of tissue interactions in animal embryos. There is much interest in the fact that some tissues adhere more or less to others in the developing organism. It is thought (although this is pure conjecture) that all the cellular movements in early development might be governed by such selective adhesions and that they might play a key role in the developmental process. This remains an exciting subject, a real frontier, and we want to know both its exact role in development and how the adhesion itself operates.

In the animal, unlike the plant, not all the reactions between tissues are concerned with growth and development. The adult animal has a significant amount of communication between tissues that plays a key role in its maintenance and functioning. This communication within the organism falls into two general categories, hormonal and neural; let us examine both. Again it is fair to say that the problems connected with these two types of interaction are at the top of the list in importance to the physiologist of today.

The study of chemical messengers, or hormones, has been active for the past forty years. By extirpation of certain glands and other more sophisticated techniques, we now have a great list of different hormones produced by a large number of glands. In the mammal, sugar balance, metabolic rate, sexual activity with all its cycles of change, blood pressure, and preparation of the body for emergency and stress are all controlled by hormones and the system of endocrine glands. More recently a similar situation has been discovered in insects and other arthropods, and the hormones there differ sufficiently so that the science of insect endocrinology is quite independent and fascinating in its own right.

The hormones are secreted directly into the blood and are carried by the general circulation of the body. This is a most efficient system, and a small amount of hormone secreted in one spot will spread over the entire animal in a short time. There is no possibility here of polar movement, such as is found in plants; the whole organism gets the message, not just one part. The fact that often it is only one part that responds, however, means that the onus for specific, selective action lies in particular tissues being sensitive to the hormone and capable of responding.

The processes that are controlled by hormones are all relatively slow ones. Some will act over a period of years, such as the growth hormone of the pituitary gland. Some will act over a period of months, such as the sex hormones connected with, for instance, the appearance of periods of sexual activity. Some will act over periods of minutes, such as the perfusion of adrenalin into our blood in moments of anger or danger. But even the shortest is not so rapid as the nerve control of processes, which we shall examine presently.

Of all the discoveries in the science of endocrinology, perhaps the most surprising is the fact that the majority of the endocrine glands do not act alone, but in conjunction with the pituitary gland. That is to say, the activity of the peripheral gland is controlled by another secretion given off by the pituitary. It is as though there were a double check on any one process. But more than that, and undoubtedly no coincidence, the pituitary is attached to the brain and therefore provides a link between the two coordinating systems. It means that nervous activity can be augmented by hormonal activity and vice versa; the two systems are completely intermeshed.

At this moment there is a new and important surge of interest in the molecular aspects of hormone action. The first step has been to attempt to identify the chemical nature of the hormones. This identification has been possible for the majority of mammalian hormones. Many hormones are proteins—for instance, insulin, the first protein molecule for which the entire atomic structure was known. Recently the chemical structure of another protein, the growth hormone, has been unraveled. The next step for the future is to understand how the hormone acts in biochemical terms. What makes certain tissues reactive to a particular hormone and not others? How does the hormone alter the metabolism of the cell so that it is changed in a specific way to produce a specific result? The biochemist is interested in these questions because for some time he has appreciated the fact that the queen of problems is the control of the biochemical reactions within cells. After learning something of these control mechanisms, he finds that the physiologist has a whole battery of chemicals, namely, the hormones, that perform very precise and specific control tasks. Clearly this is another place to attack, and we find that the biochemist is vigorously looking at every place within the superstructure of biological science where he might ply his trade and gain new important insights, as he has in biochemical genetics.

There is even talk now of attacking the problem of neurophysiology on the molecular level. There has been controversy and doubt concerning recent claims that information on how to turn in a simple maze can be fed into a flatworm by extracting the ribonucleic acid from worms that have learned and feeding it into those that have not. But the reported benefit from this special diet is marginal, and the matter needs much further study. Yet the biochemist, buoyed by the wonderful success he has achieved in other areas, feels that it is basically not outrageous to consider memory and other attributes of the central nervous system in terms of molecular explanations. Certainly the practical interest in mental disorders can sensibly be approached on a chemical basis, and this is being pursued in numerous laboratories. It is reasonable to expect that some mental conditions have a biochemical explanation. Indeed there are well-known examples, such as idiocy resulting from phenylketonuria. This disease is caused by a single mutation which results in the accumulation of phenylpyruvic acid, a substance that has a most adverse effect on the brain. Other disorders might also have a chemical or metabolic basis, but the number of substances being so numerous, and their amounts being so small, the elucidation of the problems may be difficult and slow.

But we must remember we are at the tissue level and not at the molecular level. We are at the level where we might show the biochemist the nature of the problem and then let him proceed with the micro-tools. With this in mind, let us go back to the tissue of the nervous system and see the prospects and the problems.

We have already pointed out that the nervous system is a complex that involves sensory organs, a central nervous system (which includes the brain), and the motor nerves (which go to the various muscles throughout the body). If we now look at this great sprawling structure from the point of view of a tissue, we find that it is made up of a large number of cells called neurons which have long, thin processes attached to them, namely, a main axon and numerous finer dendrites. These neurons are so arranged that the fine branching processes of one will lie in close proximity to those of another in what is known as a synapse. The result is that an impulse can travel from one neuron to another, bridging the synapse on the way.

When we come to the cell level, we will have something to say about the mechanism of the propagation of the impulse as it passes down the fiber, but here we are concerned with the more general aspect of the traveling of the impulse through the whole tissue. This transmission brings up two important properties of nerve networks: one is that the impulse moves in a directional, or polar, fashion, and the other is that when two or more neurons are connected with a single one, the impulse may not necessarily go into all the neurons, for the synapses are capable of making the pathways selective.

The fact that the impulse moves in a polar fashion is not due to a special property of the nerve, but to the architecture of the nerve net, and to the ability of the synapse to operate as a directional valve and only permit impulses to go one way. There is still some debate as to how this is managed, although the traditional view is that a substance is released at the end of the neuron which bridges the synaptic gap and activates the second neuron. If this substance is only produced by one of the neurons and not the other, clearly one has a directional valve. It is presumed that the chemical acetyl choline is concerned with this gap-bridging process, although there is also some recent evidence that electrical events may be instrumental in crossing the synaptic gap. There remains the further problem of how, if more than one nerve enters a synapse, the impulse can selectively go on to some of the attached neurons and not others. The synapse acts not only as a valve in the sense that it permits flow in one direction but it serves as a switch also.

The use of language borrowed from electronic engineers is deliberate, for great advances in the understanding of the nervous system in the last twenty years have come not only from physiological studies, but from the mathematics of communication systems. Information theory has made great strides and has resulted in enormous progress in computers and other types of information-storage and processing machines. Always, during the course of this work, there was a strong consciousness of the relevance of these ideas to the working of the mammalian brain. Furthermore, there persists the feeling today that the limit of this approach has by no means been reached and that as a field it holds great promise for the future.

The design of an electrical circuit can itself produce qualities which are known to exist in the nervous system of animals. We have already mentioned the existence of valves and switches, and besides these there is the notion of feedback control. If a circuit is made so that the end result is fed back into the beginning of the circuit, then the circuit itself will modify its behavior according to the end result. Another physiological process that can be easily manufactured by electronic circuits is memory, or information storage.

All these mathematical and electrical studies serve as models for the nervous system. Therefore one of the great questions for the future is how does the brain actually work; which model does it most closely resemble, and in what ways does it differ from the model?

The problem of how the nervous system operates is being attacked in a number of different ways. One of the approaches is to attempt to discover what kind of information is being sent in from the sense organ; only this way can one grasp what kind of material the brain must work with. For instance, in the examination of the chemical sense, it is known that the receptors will be stimulated by a particular kind of substance—sweet, sour, bitter, and salty in the case of humans. From these four classes of receptors one must be able to discern the whole variety of tastes in cooking. How is this possible? Presumably it is by the playing of these four notes into some kind of taste melody. The situation of taste reception in some caterpillars has been examined, and here the nerves that come from the taste organs can be isolated in small bundles. If the sense organs are provided with a variety of stimuli, it is possible in each case to record what kinds of impulses pass down the nerves. The frequency and the amplitude, or vigor, of the impulse on the nerves is different for different receptors, and therefore different kinds of information are sent to the brain. To use the modern jargon, this is the code. And next comes the great question of how the code is read in the brain and converted into what we call odor and taste sensations. The study has begun with the logical question: What messages are sent to the brain? Next we must ask how the brain processes these messages, another problem for the future.

We have already mentioned that the brain is affected by chemical substances, but there also is evidence that certain substances in specific areas of the brain have specific actions. It has been shown, for instance, that the introduction of minute amounts of sex hormones in very small restricted areas of the hypothalamus region of the brain will produce immediate sexual activity. Therefore hormones are not only connected in their function with the nervous system through the pituitary gland at the base of the brain, but the hormones exist and operate apparently in the brain itself. We have therefore a picture of not only great complexity on the score of nerve pathways, but also in the chemical reactions that take place within the brain. It is a striking example of the fact that organized activity comes from the structure of a tissue as well as its chemical composition, and in this case both the structure and the number of chemicals involved are vast and complex.

To drive this point home, let me again cite an example that was mentioned previously. If an eye of a newt is removed and replaced upside down, all the severed fibers of the neurons will find their proper connection again even though they will have to curve 180 degrees. It is as though one had a cable with wires of many colors that was cut, and in the splice each wire was hooked back to the one of the same color in the opposite cable. The only difference here is that instead of a dozen connections, there are hundreds of connections, and instead of someone looking at the matching colors and tying them up, they grow and of their own accord find the right connection. How do they do this? Has each nerve got special chemical properties, or special electrical properties, and if this is so how do they find the proper junction among the maze of other fibers? It may be that there are other equally amazing and wonderful phenomena in nature, but this thought does not lessen one's desire to know the answer to how the nervous system manages all these remarkable feats.

It is quite possible, and is firmly believed by many biologists, that the answer will lie in analyzing the system in smaller units. The unit the next size down is the cell; in the case of the nervous system, the neuron.

9

THERE IS NO DOUBT THAT ONE OF THE GREAT DIS-
coveries of biology, made by Schleiden and Schwann in the
middle of the last century, is that all living organisms are made up of
cells. Today it seems to us so well known and so obvious that it may
be hard to imagine why this is an important or significant fact. It is
almost taken for granted, and there is some mild wonder as to why
Schleiden and Schwann created such a stir.

However, with a moment's reflection, its significance is not hard to
see. It means, first of all, that in the development of a multicellular
organism, growth involves cell division, the repeated splitting of cells
in two as they grow. The cell is therefore the construction unit in
growth. Furthermore the cell has a nucleus which contains chromosomes, the repository of genetic information. By mitosis this nucleus
divides so that each chromosome is exactly duplicated and each
daughter cell has the complete genetic complement.

Besides being the unit of growth and heredity, the cell is also the

A Cell

THESE are rod cells from the retina. In the lower portion of each, one can see a nucleus in the bulging region. Also note that below there is a complex connection (synapse) with the fiber from a connecting nerve cell. At the top of the cell (and partly cut off) there are layers of macromolecules specifically involved in the absorbing of light. When light hits these pigment layers a chemical reaction occurs, which is recorded by a nerve impulse that travels down the cell and across the connection to the nerve cell below. The length of the portion of the rod cells shown here is about 30 microns (0.03 millimeters). This is drawn from photographs taken with the electron microscope.

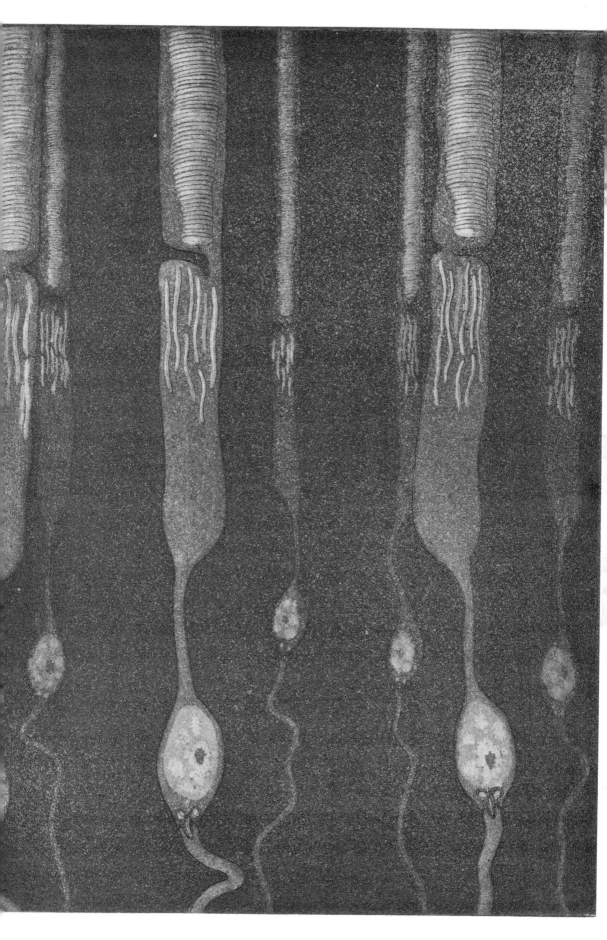

unit of metabolism. By metabolism we mean the conversion of energy. In other words, we are saying that the cell, as a unit, is a minute motor. This emphasizes the importance of size, for without maintaining a critical size, the cell could not run. In order for gases to diffuse and chemical reaction to take place, it is necessary to have the reactants properly placed with relation to one another. Without this special organization it would be impossible to operate the cell properly as an energy machine. The force of this argument is becoming increasingly clear as we learn more about the specific chemical reactions that take place within a cell, and there is circumstantial evidence in the fact that cells from all organisms, large and small, are roughly the same size.

There is one important exception to this rule: bacteria are much smaller than the cells of all other animals and plants. They differ also in their internal architecture: their nucleus is quite different and not comparable to the complex one of higher cells, and they utterly lack certain structures in their cytoplasm. Their principal chemical components, however, are the same as higher cells; it is simply that they are arranged in a different fashion, and there is considerable evidence that this difference is related to the size difference.

In the past, great issue has been made of the fact that certain cells such as bacteria and protozoa are complete organisms, while other cells are merely part of a multicellular organism. Today we do not find this distinction so remarkable; for the cell in both instances is a unit of metabolism and a unit of heredity. The only difference is that in multicellular organisms, following cell division, the daughter cells stick together, and in the protozoa they do not. This latter point may be of great significance, but it says nothing about special attributes of the whole versus parts. For instance, separate unicellular organisms can interact by producing substances that affect one another, but when this same process occurs in tissue, the kind of control achieved is far greater for the simple reason that the structural relation of the cells, due to their adhesiveness, is controllable and predictable. According to this view, the differences between single cells and cells in masses is purely a mechanical one, although a mechanical difference with far-reaching consequences.

In considering the parts of the cell in more detail, we have already noted the fact that the nucleus contains the genes, which, depending upon the cytoplasmic environment, give off messages that affect the cytoplasm. The nucleus, therefore, is not a site of energy turnover, but a sort of signal station. There are, however, cells which function admirably without their nucleus, such as the red blood cells of mammals and the sieve tubes in the phloem of higher plants. These cells respire, that is, convert energy—and with it perform specific tasks which benefit the whole organism. The only thing they have lost with their nucleus is the ability to divide and spawn other cells. In a sense they have become so specialized that they have lost their powers of reproduction.

In the cytoplasm of the cell, there are many structures. Some are associated with nuclear activity, such as the centrioles, which are connected with cell division; and others, such as mitochondria, are associated with the respiratory activity of the cell. The mitochondrion is a minute chemical factory which is primarily responsible for the burning of the fuel in a careful and controlled fashion so that the energy can be used for all the activities of the cell. In plant cells there are also the green plastids, which perform a similar function except that they convert the radiant energy of the sun to useful energy for the organism.

In the past twenty years there have been two parallel interests in the cell constituents. One is the biochemical approach: Which enzymes and enzyme systems are found in which cytoplasmic structures? The principle techniques have involved the destruction of the cell, the isolation of certain functional parts, and the analysis of their chemical composition. The other is old-fashioned cell morphology, but the reason for the new interest is that our conception of the morphology has been completely revolutionized by the advent of the electron microscope.

With a light microscope, because of the properties of light itself, it is not possible to resolve objects smaller than one or two microns. With the electron microscope one can see objects as small as 50 Angstrom units, a resolution which is over a thousand times greater than the light microscope. At first, in the 1940's, this great magnification seemed ineffectual because cells could not be properly fixed and prepared for viewing, but over the past twenty years the techniques have been improved, and now we can see all sorts of things that had never been seen before. The excitement has been that of exploring the unknown. The big task of the future, however, is to correlate specific structures with specific chemicals. We want now not only to know what the cell looks like but what this appearance means in terms of chemical construction. We do not merely want to see the cans which are stacked on the grocer's shelf; we want to be able to read the labels on the cans.

But even more important than this to the cell biologist is an understanding of how the cell functions, how it uses its energy for the various kinds of specialized activity, such as locomotion or coordination. The most stubborn of all these problems has been the question of how cells move. There are, of course, numerous types of cell motion: amoeboid motion, protoplasmic streaming, the movement of cilia, muscular contraction. Of these, muscular contraction has provided the most information, largely because of the work on the biochemistry of muscle activity. It is known that muscle protein molecules are contractile with the addition of an energy-providing substance, and that the reactions can take place with the chemicals isolated from the muscle. The task of putting these substances in their proper place in the muscle and discovering from electron-microscope and polarizing-microscope studies how the molecules actually do their work in the normal muscle has been an exceedingly difficult one, not yet wholly resolved.

Research into the mechanism of ciliary movement has taken a step forward recently because of electron microscopy. A cross section of a motile cilium or a flagellum shows a circle of nine pairs of tubules which surround a central pair, a picture that was impossible to show with the light microscope. Furthermore, with especially good preparations it is possible to see that the pairs of tubules have two small projections, or spurs. It has been shown that these spurs are a special energy-providing chemical, and there is other evidence that the paired tubes are the contractile protein. But even with this splendid new information, we are uncertain as to how the tubules contract and how the chemical on the spurs facilitates the contraction. It is also well known that cilia will have a directional beat and a different kind of stroke forward and backward. It is presumed that these controls are achieved by instructions from the basal body found at the end of the cilium, but what they in fact do is unknown.

The literature on amoeboid movement is vast, and the number of theories is an exponential function of the number of facts. To begin with some solid information, contractile proteins have been extracted from amoebae and from larger slime molds that have massive amoeboid movements. It is possible to show with polarized light and electron microscopy that in the moving pseudopods there are microtubules which seem to be oriented in the direction of movement. Depending upon the type of amoeba, there is either a thick or a thin gel or solid surface layer; inside this the cytoplasm is fluid, yet clearly not a homogeneous fluid, but loaded with solid and viscous matter, as can be shown from its flow pattern.

We could greatly extend the list of facts, but instead let me briefly list some of the hypothetical conclusions which have been reached by the workers in the field. There is a general agreement that the contraction probably takes place in the gel layer, even when it is exceedingly thin. There is no agreement as to whether the contraction occurs in the posterior end, thereby squeezing the cell forward, or whether the contraction occurs at the anterior end, pulling the cell forward. There is a growing opinion that different amoebae may in fact move by different means and there is not one universal mechanism. But the basic question of the exact position of the contractile protein and how it effects the movement is still unresolved, even though this is a problem which has occupied the energies of many cell physiologists for almost a hundred years.

Besides the movement of amoebae, there are other organisms that move without any visible means of propulsion. Diatoms, some blue-green algae such as *Oscillatoria,* and a number of different bacteria move without cilia, pseudopods, or any form of contractile appendages. Again this has been known for a long time, and we do not seem to be any closer to the solution of how these move than we were years ago. The progress in the physiology of cell locomotion has been slow, yet the desire to answer these questions remains. All locomotion will continue, therefore, to be an area of active research, and it can only be hoped that, as with the biochemistry of muscular contraction, there will soon be a significant advance in the understanding of all types of cell movement.

One aspect of the movement of single cells is important to mention here. The smaller the cell, the slower it moves, that is, if one considers the fastest cells known for any one size level. This relation actually holds for multicellular organisms also, for small organisms cannot achieve the rate of speed of larger ones. This principle applies only over a large size-range and applies equally for swimming, running, or flying animals. Maximum speed is achieved in animals about a meter long or more, such as tuna fish, cheetahs, and swans. At the other end of the scale, there are minute bacteria whose rate of movement is very slow.

Besides moving, cells transmit impulses, and this, as we have already seen, is the prime activity of the neuron. It is possible to make a model of a nerve by dipping an iron wire in a solution of nitric acid; when one end of the wire is scratched, a wave slowly progresses down the surface of the wire. This wave consists of a local chemical reaction which moves forward only because it has already used up the surface reactants behind and they have not yet had time to regenerate. This is a good model of a nerve impulse in that the energy for the transmission lies on the surface and can be restored on the surface, giving a wave of depolarization followed by a period of recovery.

The classic way to study the nerve impulse is to have it pass over a recording electrode and watch the electrical disturbance on an oscilloscope as the impulse passes the electrode. But it is known that the nerve is not an iron wire, and the question arises as to what kind of a chemical reaction is taking place which would result in the wave that is the nerve impulse. It is now known that as the wave passes there is a sudden release of potassium ions to the outside, and sodium ions which surround the nerve diffuse inward. The recovery period is a period of pumping, where the potassium is brought back in and the sodium rejected from the neuron fiber. The recovery needs energy, for these ions are being pushed against diffusion gradients. The matter that is still not clear is what kind of an event can suddenly open up the cell membrane so that these ions escape. In the case of the pumping back of the ions against concentration gradients, there is increasing evidence that this is accomplished by enzymes which literally grab the ions and release them on the other side, a process that performs work and therefore requires energy.

What is known of the nerve impulse and what is not known focuses our attention on the cell surface. The whole study of cell permeability, of which the nerve impulse is but one aspect, is a very active field. In order to function, cells must constantly pass things in and out, and the question as to how this occurs is vital. Many substances are known to pass in and out by the simple process of diffusion, and in some cases it is even possible to build up gradients of the substance if it is removed inside the cell by some sort of chemical combination and can no longer act to repel molecules of its own kind. Other substances are brought in by enzyme action, as we have just seen, and the importance of this active transport, as it is called, has been increasingly recognized.

The matter of permeability plays an important role in the nervous system for another reason. Chemoreceptors, that is, taste and smell receivers, are so designed that they can record certain specific kinds of chemicals. Some receptor cells respond to sweetness, some to bitterness, and so forth. How this is effected is not known, but it is assumed that there is some property of the surface of the receptor especially designed to receive certain classes of molecules. The argument in this fascinating question centers around the problem of what properties of the molecules evoke the response. There are those who suggest that it is a lock-and-key process: the receptor has a surface mold of a certain shape that can receive only certain forms of molecules, and when one of these snaps into place, the response signal is fired off. Another view is that the resonance of the molecule, the vibration of its atoms, produces key responses in specific cells. There are other hypotheses, but again we need more information before the question can be satisfactorily resolved.

Another kind of permeability has aroused considerable interest recently. This is the passing of large molecules into the cell. It is now known that the nuclear membrane has large holes in it which can permit macromolecules to pass through it, but the cell membrane does not show such a perforated structure. Instead, the large molecules are engulfed by the cell, much as an amoeba will engulf a bacterium. This micro-engulfment is called pinocytosis, and it has been shown that this is a common ability of cells. It is doubtful, however, that this is the only way large substances can be made to enter a cell, although we know of no other at the moment.

In order to fully understand permeability and all the other phenomena associated with the cell surface, it is necessary to have a better understanding of its structure. We know, largely by inference from permeability experiments and from biochemical analysis of cell surfaces, that the membrane of the cell must consist of a mixture of proteins and fatlike substances (phospholipids). But what we do not know (although there are reasonable conjectures) is precisely how these substances are placed, and how permeability changes will alter the surface, or how the active transport sites are constructed. One of the reasons we do not know this is that the surface is too fine to see in any detail with the electron microscope. It is known that the membrane itself is very thin and that when two cells are in contact the membranes become very intimate and lie exceedingly close to one another. But this tells us nothing of the molecular structure and how it performs its tasks, which are so important to the existence and proper functioning of the cell.

We have therefore in this discussion of the cell and its surface come down to a size we can no longer see, even in the electron microscope, yet our questions have not diminished, but if anything increased. Let us now enter the world of macromolecules, the world that has generated such extraordinary excitement in the last twenty years of biology.

Macromolecules

10

THERE ARE A NUMBER OF DIFFERENT KINDS OF large molecules, and their study has led to more than one branch of chemistry. As we shall see, so many of the properties of macro-molecules differ from those of smaller molecules that the study of the larger ones has become a specialized science.

One kind of macromolecule is the polymer. In this class a small molecule is the unit, which is repeated over and over again to make a larger unit. The polymer chemist is interested in the mechanism which permits these small molecules to hook together in long chains, as well as the practical consequence of his ability to synthesize new kinds of substances. The chemist's ingenuity in making artificial polymers has been outstanding, and we have many new synthetic substances, such as nylon and orlon.

There are many natural polymers to be found within living orga-nisms. For instance, latex is composed of repeating units of neoprene, a small and relatively simple compound. More common, and also

Macromolecules

THIS is an imaginary drawing of an orderly array of the light-sensitive macromolecules in a rod cell. They are too small to be seen in any detail with the electron microscope and at the same time have not yet yielded to crystallographic techniques for revealing structure. The periodicity of the layers is about 340 Angstrom units (0.034 microns) .

The haze between the solid layers of macromolecules represents the masses of smaller molecules which are found inside cells.

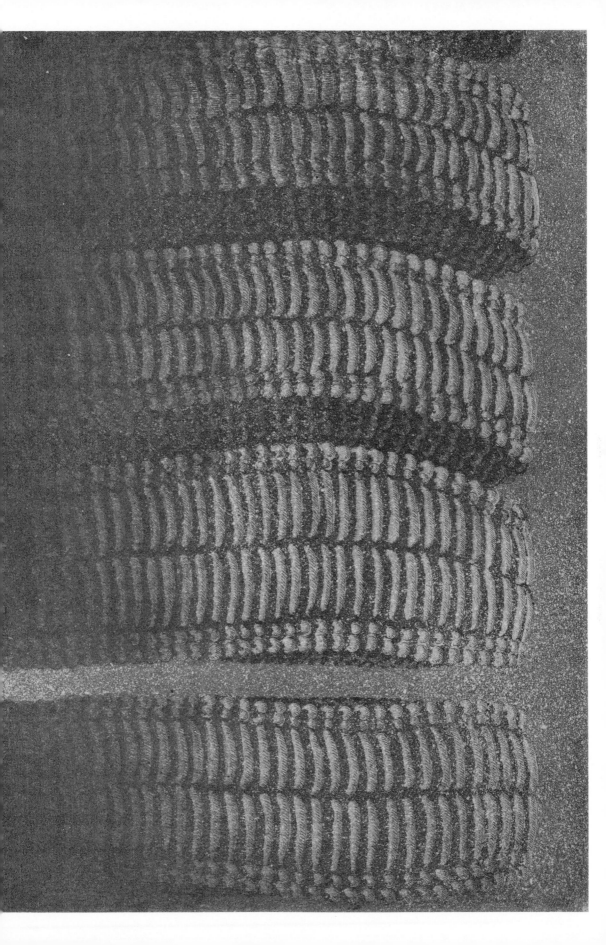

found in plants, is cellulose, which is made up of repeating units of the sugar glucose. Sugars can easily polymerize and form plant and animal starches and chitin, which is basically a polysaccharide although it does contain some nitrogen. In organisms, then, polymers serve as both supporting, skeletal materials and as food storage. In the case of the former, chitin and cellulose are difficult to break down, and resistant to change. In the storage substance starch, the sugar can be polymerized or depolymerized with the greatest of ease, depending upon whether the organism needs to accumulate or use its reserves.

One of the surprising things about large molecules is that the majority of them are connected with life and living organisms. We have already mentioned carbohydrate polymers, but even more important are proteins. It has been generally accepted for a long time that they are the major architectural substances of cells, and a vast amount of research has been done on them. More recently the nucleic acids have taken the center of the stage, not so much because of their abundance in cells, but because of their key role in the living process. Finally there are many other somewhat smaller but still large substances which are biologically important, such as the porphyins, which are part of hemoglobin in blood and chlorophyll in photosynthetic plants, various vitamins, and a host of lesser cell constituents.

To begin with the proteins, the initial question that arose concerned their size and shape. All the classical methods of the chemist devised to study small molecules were ineffective. The first important advance in research into protein structure was made some thirty years ago by Theodor Svedberg, who developed a special high-speed centrifuge and used it for determining size and molecular weights. It was found that their weights varied from 2 million to very small proteins in the neighborhood of 10,000. By other techniques it was discovered that proteins varied in shape: some were globular, some spindle-shaped, and some were long and thin in external outline.

It had been known before that proteins were made up of a series of amino acid units attached together, and years ago it was possible, in the laboratory, to hook a few amino acids together to make small bits of proteins. For large proteins, however, there was no inkling as to how or in what sequence the amino acids were arranged. One could determine the amino acid content of a protein by the simple expedient of breaking up the protein into its constituted amino acids and identifying them. This process was at first laborious, but now, with the use of chromatography, a large amount of information can be gathered accurately and quickly. Also it is possible to split proteins using proteolytic enzymes, and by picking a small protein molecule, such as insulin, to reconstruct the complete sequence of amino acids in the entire protein. It was discovered that the insulin molecule was made up of 51 amino acids.

But there is more to the structure of a protein than its internal sequence of amino acids and its overall contour. The chains of amino acids must fold in and about one another to give a three-dimensional shape. The folding, sometimes in a helix, is reinforced by special bonds which hold it together. If the protein is denatured, these bonds are broken, and while the whole molecule is intact, its physical and chemical properties are totally different. The fact that the white of an egg or milk proteins become utterly different after heating are homely examples of this general principle. There is at the moment great interest among physical chemists in these problems because it is evident that many key biological processes are dependent not only upon the composition of the proteins involved, but upon their configuration as well.

This point has nowhere been more evident than in the analysis of nucleic acids. That these substances existed in nuclei has been known for a long time; in fact, their name stems from this early observation. As with proteins, the first information was on their chemical components. It was known that they consisted of a backbone of five carbon sugars, onto which were added bases (purines and pyrimidines). The total number of bases was four for any one nucleic acid, and there has been success in analyzing the exact sequence of bases for any one nucleic acid.

But the great advance came when J. D. Watson and F. H. C. Crick showed, from X-ray analyses, that the nucleic acid existed in a double helix: two backbones of sugar molecules with the bases paired off in a very specific way. This immediately suggested a method of replication, for, by uncoiling the helix, the separate strands can regenerate a new partner which again produces a double helix. It is especially clear in the thin single-strand (single double helix) chromosome of bacteria. For instance, it has been shown that when a chromosome duplicates preparatory to cell division, the genes duplicate at one end first and then proceed like a zipper down the chromosome. It has even been possible to show partially duplicated chromosomes in electron microphotographs in the circular chromosomes of some bacteria.

Most of this work has been so recent largely because macromolecules are too small to be seen properly and too large to lend themselves to all the older, standard methods of the chemist which were devised for small molecules. The first step in this new era was the high-speed centrifuge, and since then other new methods, persistence, and clever analysis have pieced together a remarkable story, but one that is still known only in fragments. The fact that it is important to know more about macromolecules can best be emphasized by showing further what some of these substances do within cells.

To begin with proteins, one of their functions undoubtedly is support, and we are correct in referring to them as architectural substances. There are some proteins of a fibrous nature that make up supporting structures; collogen, the principal ingredient of tendons, is an excellent example. But more than that, if we took any cell and dissolved away all the proteins, leaving the other substances, the cell would vanish and no more than a rubble of chemicals would be left.

From the point of view of the functioning of the cell, the cornerstone of all living processes is enzymes. Enzymes are proteins which catalyze and control all or almost all of the chemical reactions within cells. All the synthesis of new compounds in growth and the degradation of compounds for obtaining energy are mediated by enzymes. The more one examines the chemistry of the cell, the more one recognizes that new chemical events are taking place, and for each of these there is an enzyme or a series of enzymes which promotes the series of reactions. The majority of enzymes are quite specific in their actions, and therefore the number of enzymes within a cell, even a small bacterial cell, is tremendous.

Let me make an aside here concerning a comparison between living and nonliving systems at this size level. If we look at fragments of space as small as a cell in a nonliving system, such as portions of a gas, a liquid, or a solid crystal, there will be a vast number of single kinds of molecules or relatively few kinds of molecules. By contrast, in the case of a cell, there will be an exceedingly large number of different kinds of molecules. This difference is a rather fundamental one, and the physicist W. M. Elsasser has pointed out that the difficulty of applying laws of physics blindly to biological systems lies in this novel character of inhomogeneity that living organisms possess. He suggests that just as there has been a theoretical physics which is based on quantum mechanics which applies only to homogeneous physical systems, so there must be a theoretical biology based upon laws derived from inhomogeneous systems.

To return to enzymes, their study has been an important branch of modern biochemistry. The interest in them has centered around a number of different problems, the most basic of which is how the enzyme latches on to the substrate, the chemical substance it will alter, and how it effects the alteration. These basic problems are still not satisfactorily resolved. All sorts of interesting information has been obtained on the rates of reaction, or enzyme kinetics, and from this many inferences are possible, but the essential steps in the enzyme reaction are not fully understood.

Another aspect of enzymology that has attracted much attention in recent years is that of enzyme induction. In many bacteria, for instance, the presence of a particular substrate will slowly cause the synthesis of the enzyme capable of utilizing or degrading the substrate and after this enzyme has accumulated, the bacterium can exist happily on this new food source. Each organism has only a limited number of inducible enzymes, but the mechanism involved in this induction remains an unsolved problem of considerable interest.

A first step in linking macromolecules with genetics came from the work of G. H. Beadle and E. L. Tatum; this was the beginning of the science of biochemical genetics, in the 1940's. They worked with the bread mold *Neurospora* and obtained mutants of this organism that failed to grow on a simple medium (as the wild type did) unless it contained a specific chemical—for example, biotin. They then showed that what ailed the mutant was that it had lost the natural ability to make its own biotin and therefore needed to have a supply of it in its growth medium. They showed, furthermore, that the reason why the mutant could not perform the synthesis was that it lacked one of the essential enzymes in the synthetic chain that produces the biotin, and from this they made the hypothesis, which still stands today, that one gene is responsible for the existence of one enzyme.

But at that time little was known about the gene and, as we have already mentioned, the developments since then have been as important as they have been exciting. We now know that genes consist of deoxyribonucleic acid (DNA), and the sequence of the four bases is a code which can be translated into the synthesis of a specific substance. It does this by imparting its coded structure to some ribonucleic acids, or messenger RNA, which leaves the nucleus and wanders to the ribosomes, which are small RNA particles in the cytoplasm. These ribosomes are coded by the messenger RNA and they, using this code, manufacture a specific protein. That is, the specific sequence of the bases in the RNA will give a specific sequence of the amino acids in the protein. This amino acid sequence is what makes one protein different from another. The protein produced may be structural or it may be an enzyme, which can now sally forth and participate in the synthesis of a specific substance, such as a carbohydrate, a fat, or some other chemical. The only thing this wonderfully simple picture of modern molecular biology lacks, but which we discussed in the previous chapter, is the structural relation of all these sequences. Clearly the spacing, the placement, and the movement of all the actors in this drama are also of key significance, and the success of the play is as dependent upon the stage as it is upon the players.

If all this is now known, are we to imagine that molecular genetics is finished as a field of endeavor and that we have made all the exciting discoveries? This is a fair question, and perhaps we can best answer it by considering what problems remain. In the first place, the one just mentioned, namely, that of the spatial architecture of all these vital components, is far from solved. We do not even know how the nucleic acids of the chromosomes of ordinary animals and plants compare with those of bacteria, although we are beginning to have some inklings. There is also evidence of different kinds of genes which do different sorts of jobs; some genes, instead of being concerned with the cytoplasm, are involved in regulating the activity of other genes. This emphasizes the fact that the molecular geneticist is no longer satisfied to learn how one gene produces one enzyme, but wants to know how the whole package of genes produces all the characters of an organism. It is the organization and control of genetic activity and the eliciting of the proper sequence of events from generation to generation that have taken on prime importance.

This organization and control problem, the reader will recognize, has a familiar ring; it is the problem of development which we discussed in considering whole organisms and the differentiation of organs and tissues. Today, in fact, developmental biology has become in part molecular biology, for it is suddenly apparent that here is a meeting ground of the two approaches. We want to be able to understand development in terms of molecules as we are able to do in the case of genetics. Here then is a place where molecular biology has the opportunity of making new and significant discoveries in the problems of growth and differentiation. There is every indication, however, that the progress must be made hand in hand with the experimental biologist so that the overall objectives are never lost in the somewhat confining perusal of the macromolecules.

There is another aspect to these large molecules that has been tremendously important, both as to the information it has given so far and as to its future. This is the science of virology. Viruses are composed of nucleic acids and proteins, and much of the basic relation between nucleic acid and protein has been verified and some aspects even demonstrated for the first time in viruses. Moreover, the study of viral infection has provided the best example known of development on a molecular level. The changes are sufficiently simple to be analyzed chemically, and it has been shown that there is a set sequence of reactions in which each one proceeds in its proper turn. This is precisely the way we imagine development to occur in higher organisms, the only difference being in the number of sequences of chemical reactions. But the future of virology is promising, for viruses provide a tool with which biochemical investigations can be made on the key macromolecules of living organisms that have been, by the very nature of viruses, dissected out from other complications which reside in the living cell.

We could go on with the discussion of what is known of macromolecules and what important problems lie in the future for a long time. The enthusiasm of the biochemist has not abated, but continues to rise, and the number of successes in molecular biology within the last twenty years fully justifies this confident attitude.

11

THE DISTINCTION BETWEEN LARGE MOLECULES and small ones is purely arbitrary. The division line is indistinct, somewhere between a molecular weight of 1,000 and 10,000. To compare the size levels of cells with large and small molecules, the smallest cell, a bacterium, would contain about 10^6 macromolecules, and a bacterium is roughly one-thousandth the mass of a cell from a higher organism. A macromolecule is made up of small molecules hooked together, as, for instance, amino acids in a protein, bases and sugars in nucleic acids, or sugars in polysaccharides. The number of small molecules in a macromolecule may vary from a few hundred to over 200,000, depending upon the size of the larger molecule. With the highest powers of the electron microscope, we can see the largest macromolecules only; all the lesser ones are too small to be detected. Therefore the only information we have about the structure of ordinary molecules is from indirect means, such as the interpretation of the diffraction pattern of their crystals.

Molecules

ALL cells are crammed full of many small molecules bouncing and jostling against each other. The principal molecule is water, which, as can be seen in the plate, has two hydrogen atoms attached to a central oxygen atom. Also shown on the plate is a larger sugar molecule and an amino acid molecule. There are other kinds of small molecules in cells (for example, salts), but they are all few in number when compared to the water molecules.

The diameter of one water molecule is about 3 Angstrom units (3×10^{-8} centimeter).

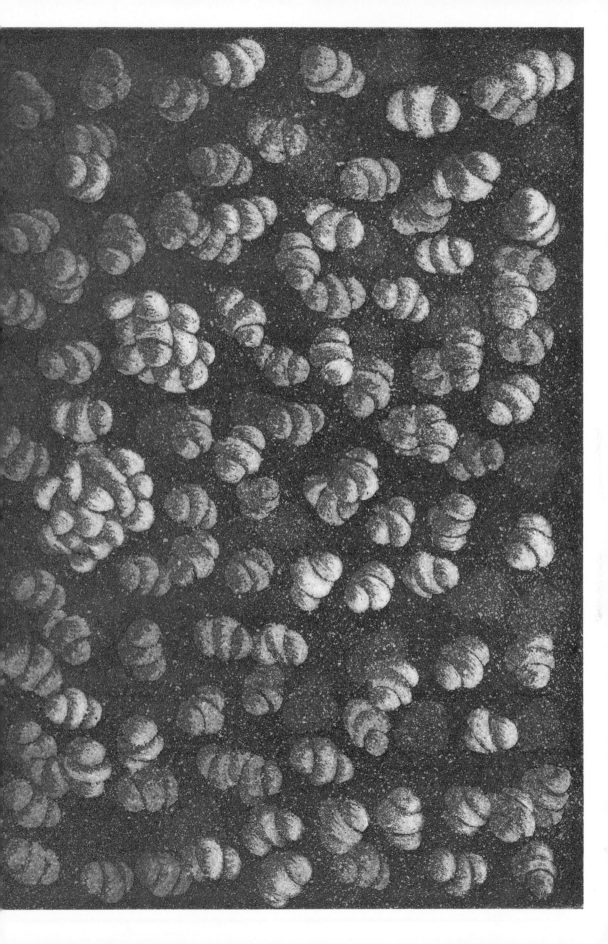

One of the greatest triumphs in the pursuit of science by man is the kinetic theory of gases. It explains so much with such little effort that in terms of satisfying the mind it has hardly any competition. The basic premise is that all molecules are in motion and that temperature is no more than a manifestation of this molecular motion. A rise in energy enters into the molecules, which affects their rate of collision with one another, which is heat. Furthermore, this explains in the simplest and most beautiful way why pressure in a gas is directly proportionate to temperature: if one increases the rate of motion of molecules, the rate at which they bombard the walls of a container will be correspondingly great.

As the temperature decreases, the energy is lessened, the rate of motion decreases, but the result gives some well-known and very important discontinuities. That is, the molecules will pass through a series of states: the gas, liquid, and solid states, each one of which is characterized by a decrease in motion, although some movement, some vibration, is always present. This is even so in the case of a crystal, where the molecules appear to lie in perfect military array.

One may ask why molecules move. It has nothing to do with the motion of the electrons of their constituent atoms. If it were possible to place one molecule, even one charged with high energy, in a perfect vacuum shielded from all radiation or any outside influence, and if it were placed without giving it a push, then it presumably would not move. But should it be knocked by another molecule, or a photon of light, then it would begin to travel and nothing would stop it; for even if it hit another molecule or a wall, it would bounce back vigorously, commensurate with the energy it contains (which would be reflected in the temperature). The reason, then, that molecules zip about with such abandon is that they always exist in a disturbed environment, and nothing will calm this disturbance unless energy is removed from the whole system by external means, thereby lowering the temperature.

The smaller the molecule, the faster it will move. This principle is most evident in a phenomenon known as Brownian movement. If one looks at a mist or a liquid containing minute particles through the highest powers of the microscope, the smallest particles seem to bounce about on an irregular course. It was Albert Einstein who showed that the rate of movement of the particle is inversely proportionate to its size, as well as depending on other obvious factors, such as the viscosity of the medium, and the temperature. The reason the particles move is that they are hit, in an uneven fashion, by molecules in the surrounding medium. The smaller the particle, the more vigorously it will be propelled following an impact with a molecule in motion.

Besides telling us much about the activities of molecules, Brownian movement has another lesson for us here. We saw, in discussing the motion of living organisms, that the smaller the animal, the slower it could move, until finally we reached the size of small bacteria; their maximum speed was no more than 1.5×10^{-3} centimeter per second. If we look at the particles affected by Brownian movement, some of which might be small aggregates of macromolecules, their speed is roughly in the same order of magnitude. But as the particle gets smaller and as we plunge below the limits of visibility from macromolecules to smaller and smaller molecules, the speed increases by an inverse relation.

There is a great difference between animal locomotion and the movement of molecules. Animals have built engines, small metabolism machines, which convert chemical energy into flagellar movement or muscle contraction. Molecules, on the other hand, have no energy-converting machine. The great advantage to such a machine is that the motion can be directed, a feature that is impossible in the random bombardment of molecules. But, aside from this gain, organisms from bacteria to whales simply could not move at all unless they made machines to do it, while molecules cannot, except in theory, remain at rest.

They come closest to having no motion when they exist in crystals, where the molecules stick together in a precise way. And it is very precise, for if a molecule has an odd, asymmetrical shape, then each molecule in the crystal can be shown to be pointing the same way. It would appear, therefore, that we have some conflicting information, for now the molecules are no longer hitting one another and fleeing apart, but are attracting one another and, furthermore, this attraction is very specific, so that all the molecules end up perfectly aligned. We said that the molecules are still in motion, yet they seem to be fairly well imprisoned. The answer is that the molecules are moving; they are in fact vibrating so that they can remain in confined spaces. These vibrations will be specific for different parts of a molecule, and if the molecules have an irregular shape and are in close proximity, their vibrations will, so to speak, beat in unison and the equivalent parts will be attracted to one another. These attraction forces between molecules, known as van der Waal's forces, act over very short distances. They are weak forces, and can be broken by raising the temperature. The oscillations of the molecules become too great for the van der Waal's forces, and the perfection of crystal is transferred into a chaotic liquid.

Crystals are characterized by having symmetrical surfaces, and their construction can be classified into a number of different categories. It was known for a long time that there is an exact number of classes, but it was not until the work of Abbé R. J. Haüy in the latter part of the eighteenth century that we knew why. He discovered a law (the law of rational indices) which describes the possible crystal shapes, and he realized that the basis of this law is the finite number of ways in which units (molecules) can be stacked. It is the fact that crystals are made out of molecules which imposes restrictions on how many crystal shapes are possible. Crystals are an ideal example of how a larger structure can be explained in terms of its microstructure.

These aspects of crystals are ancient ones, and their importance today lies in the techniques that they have spawned. While the wave length of light is too long to resolve something so small as a molecule, this is not the case for X rays. By striking a crystal with a glancing beam of X rays, a diffraction pattern can be obtained, and this pattern reflects the structure of the space lattice within the crystal. It is possible, by complex mathematical analysis, to reconstruct the spacing of the atoms within both small and even relatively large molecules, and the great value is that the exact configuration of the molecule can be calculated. This has been and will continue to be a key tool in structural analysis of molecules.

The study of molecules is, of course, primarily the science of chemistry, and one of the main concerns of that science is the matter of how molecules react or combine. There are a number of aspects to the problem of which the most fundamental is the nature of the bonds between the atoms. We talked previously of the van der Waal's forces that kept whole molecules close to one another, but now we are talking about much stronger, tighter bonds that hold the atoms together within a molecule.

The key lies in the structure of the atom itself. The atom is composed of shells of electrons, and should the outside shell not be filled with a complete complement of electrons, the substance is capable of combining with other substances (which also have appropriate electron-deficient slots in the outer shells of their atoms). The combining of the two atoms and the use of each other's electrons is mutually satisfying. For instance, the oxygen atom lacks two electrons in its outer shell, but by combining with two hydrogen atoms, each of which has a single electron available, H_2O is formed. This is a remarkably stable molecule because all the electrons are in one complete shell that has no room for further electrons.

The bonds that hold the atoms together can only be broken and changed to new combinations with an exchange of energy. Some chemical reactions give off energy and others need energy to force them to take place. The rate at which the reaction occurs, the energy required or liberated, and what this means in terms of the bonds are of prime concern to the physical chemist who wishes to learn precisely and completely the relation between the structure of molecules and their reactivity.

Another aspect of chemistry is concerned with the study of which kinds of compounds exist and what their chemical and physical properties are. The most fertile field in this direction is organic chemistry, the chemistry of carbon compounds. Carbon, which can take on four more electrons in its outer shell, has unparalleled powers of combining with other substances, especially hydrogen, oxygen, nitrogen, and itself. The result is that the number of carbon compounds exceeds the number of compounds of all other substances, and this fact alone makes organic chemistry an exceedingly complex subject.

There are many aspects of the chemistry of carbon compounds that we could mention, but let me isolate two. First there is the problem of analyzing the atomic constitution of organic molecules. Since living organisms are made up almost entirely of carbon compounds, and since the number of substances in any one organism are legion, the opportunities for the analytic chemist are without end and fraught with technical problems of the greatest difficulty. Their solution is not only important to the biologist, but to the chemist as well, for nature has in its own laboratory synthesized an extraordinary number of different kinds and classes of compounds, the structure and the reactivity or even possible existence of which would never have been known had they not first been isolated from living organisms and identified.

The second aspect of carbon compounds that has been important is their synthesis in the laboratory. In some cases this has been of commercial or practical value, for it is easier and more effective to make a substance by synthesis from easily available substances than to extract it from vast quantities of protoplasm. In other cases the value has come from the synthesis itself, the learning of how certain compounds can be forced to combine in specific ways, thereby revealing something of the properties of molecules and their bonds. Sometimes the value has been in synthesizing new substances that have never been known to exist in nature.

The nature of matter is an endless question to the physicist and the chemist, and their search is intense at all levels: the molecule, the atom, and inside the atom. If we seem to know more at the larger, molecular level, this may be simply because of its greater size. Yet there is a strange feeling that what we do know is not enough, and that we must probe further into the properties of molecules. To a large extent, and again we come to the reductionist approach, the properties of molecules are sought in the properties of atoms, as we have already indicated in the discussion of electron shells. But there are other properties of molecules that seem very much a result of the way the atoms are put together.

A familiar example is the benzene ring. Some years ago it was shown that benzene, which is made up of six carbon atoms and six hydrogen atoms (C_6H_6), is constructed in the form of a hexagonal ring. There is another compound, hexadiyene, which has the same constituent molecules (C_6H_6) but is constructed in a straight chain, the six carbons being in a row. Despite the fact that the molecules are made up of the same atoms, their chemical and physical properties are radically different. They are unlike with respect to melting point, boiling point, density, odor, etc., and their ability to combine chemically could not be more different. The moral therefore is that not only are the component units of a substance important, but so is their structural arrangement. Another example is on a supermolecular level: carbon crystals can form in two different ways (at two different temperatures). One will give the incredibly hard structure of diamond; the other will give the slippery black greaselike substance, graphite. The difference is very real (especially on an engagement ring), but they are both made of the same atoms.

In this case there is no reason to believe that these differences cannot also be interpreted in terms of the microstructure of the atoms. There is no need for any holistic mystery here, but rather a search for a deeper understanding of the relation among the structure of atoms and molecules and the chemical and physical properties of substances. The science of molecules has not yet run its course; there are still important principles, large and small, which will be uncovered.

12

WHEN I FIRST STUDIED CHEMISTRY AT SCHOOL, IT seemed to me that we spent all year learning quaint information about various sorts of substances and then suddenly at the end of the course it all fitted into place in one great flash when we discussed the periodic table. Atoms, that is, the elements, up to that moment were not more than a heterogeneous shopping list, but all at once they became beautifully ordered. The beauty was the fact that the atomic number, which is a mark of the number of electrons (and corresponding protons in the nucleus), can place the elements in a series beginning with hydrogen, which has one electron, and going up to the heaviest elements that have been synthesized recently. The next glorious revelation was the fact that if this series is plotted against any particular physical property, such as melting point or boiling point, there is a recurrence of the properties. This periodicity (hence the name of the table) was a reflection of how many electrons were absent from the outer shell of electrons; and, furthermore, it was shown that the chemical reactivity properties varied with the filling of this peripheral shell. For instance, if the shell is complete and contains its full complement of electrons, then we have substances which are chemically almost totally inert (that is, neon, argon, krypton—the inert gases).

From the point of view of classification, one can place the different kinds of atoms in a linear number series which exactly reflects the number of electrons they contain. The arrangement of shells in layers means that one can further make a subclassification of atoms according to the degree of saturation of the outer layer.

But the periodic law is more than a system of classification. It is a principle which is almost perfect in that it is able to interpret phenomena on one level in terms of the level below. One can even predict, as was done when the periodic law was first discovered, physical and chemical properties of unknown elements, and when later these elements were discovered, the predictions were completely accurate.

With one problem solved, there is always a deeper one. In this case it was the question of the causes of the positioning of the electrons, for they not only surround the nucleus, but do so in the ordered layers. This is a problem on an even lower size level: to interpret the structure of the atom in terms of its microstructure.

Atomic physics has developed with great speed during the course of this century and has become certainly one of the greatest triumphs of man's detective ingenuity. The first step was to show that the mass of the atom was not equally distributed, but that it contained a highly dense nucleus of a positive charge surrounded by a cloud of negative electrons. This fact was established by an unusual combination of ingenious experiments and mathematical deduction (as is true of so many that I will briefly mention). I will not here enter into the evidence, but atomic physics has combined mathematical and experimental skills to a degree unknown in any other science. The success of this approach has been so remarkable that many believe it is the way to attack the future problems of biology and other fields as well.

An Atom

THIS is a fanciful picture of a hydrogen atom. The atom has a diameter of about 2 Angstrom units (2×10^{-8} centimeter). The nucleus and the electron are minute by comparison. The nucleus has a diameter of 10^{-12} centimeter, that is, roughly 100,000 times smaller; in fact, the centrally located nucleus is too small to draw to scale. The electron is constantly moving about the nucleus, and the density of the white on the plate indicates the frequency the electron is likely to be in any one area over a period of time.

The electrons travel about the nucleus at great speed, a speed, in fact, sufficient to counteract the tendency of the nucleus to pull them in by electrostatic force. Using this fact, it has been possible to calculate the speed of the electron, which is in the order of 10^7 centimeters per second.

At first it was assumed that each atom was like a miniature solar system and that the laws of electromagnetism would be sufficient to explain the properties of atoms. The realization that this was not so marks the great rise of modern atomic physics. The evidence was that if atoms were hit by light, they did not change in a continuous fashion (at least at low energies), but their energy level either remained the same or jumped to another fixed level. Furthermore, if an atom was altered in some way, it would recover, so that it was again restored to its former self. If the earth were speeded up, slowed down, or altered in its position by some gigantic extraneous force, there would never be any recovery to our original orbit. The fact that atoms are different from planets and stars led to the development of quantum mechanics. This is a mathematical method of describing the energy states which exist in discrete levels within the atom.

The stability of atoms as structures is at the core of our modern ideas. We have already mentioned the fact that the atom can recover after being disturbed; it has remarkable powers of recovery. The only way in which this stable structure can be destroyed is by raising the energy to such great heights that the atoms vary continuously rather than exist at specific energy states. We have already discussed these high-energy atoms, for they are formed in plasma, the condition achieved at fantastically high temperature such as that found in the interior of the sun. At all reasonable lower temperatures the atom is a beautifully stable and organized unit.

The understanding of the activities of electrons surrounding the nucleus has produced some startling information. The electrons appeared to have wavelike properties as well as the properties of particles. This apparent contradiction was solved by E. Schroedinger, who in 1926 showed that the electrons vibrate in standing waves within the atom, and that the pattern of vibration depended upon the amount of energy, or the quantum state, of the nucleus. These patterns of electron vibration are considered to be at the very basis of all higher structure, for they are the part of the atom, as we have already emphasized, which is responsible for their collaboration with other atoms to form molecules.

Quantum mechanics permitted a wholly new view into the activities of these unfamiliar and unobservable phenomena. It is not enough to say that the planetary view of atoms is inadequate; one wants to know how and in what way. One of the consequences of these considerations has been the uncertainty principle of Werner Heisenberg, which more than anything isolates the problem of dealing with the micro-world of atoms. Small particles can only really be discussed in terms of probabilities, and therefore statements about atoms always concern a population of atoms; one cannot make accurate predictions about any one atom, or any one electron. This is the basis of Heisenberg's principle; he pointed out that if one determines the exact position of an electron, one cannot know its velocity; or the reverse, if one knows its velocity, it is impossible to determine its position. Statistical predictions, on the other hand, are possible, provided they involve many electrons or many atoms.

To some extent this means that in this minuscule world it is impossible to follow the steps of any single particle. Instead, one must consider the activities of many molecules, and these can be described in terms of molecular behavior in any one energy or quantum state. Only the population problems have meaning and not the problems of the individual constituent atoms.

Curiously enough, this quality of the smaller parts of the universe makes them unique. For here we have almost by definition denied reductionism. Quantum mechanics is a holistic approach, and it says that if the properties of atoms are looked at in terms of single atoms, no information will be forthcoming. Atomic physicists are therefore less inclined to depend utterly upon reductionist approaches, largely because of the tremendous success they have achieved with their population approaches. The previous time in our scale of sizes, when this generalized approach appeared to be profitable and hold promise for the future, was in the discussion of animal populations and their bearing on ecology and evolution. It is difficult to know, in the case of atoms, what future there is for further discovery. Certainly one of the most active fields, and one which we have already touched upon to some degree, is the nature and the behavior of the elementary particles, especially within the atom, of which the electron is only one.

13

I T IS DIFFICULT TO SEPARATE A DISCUSSION OF THE atom from that of elementary particles, for one is so much a part of the other. We have already dwelt upon some aspects of the electron, and here we will add some information on the particles within the nucleus.

Concerning size and speed, a photon, which is a particle of light, travels at 3×10^{10} centimeters per second (186,300 miles per second) and has no mass or electrical charge. An electron can travel at any speed not exceeding that of light; it has a mass of 9×10^{-28} gram. The electron is negatively charged and attracted to a positively charged proton which resides in the nucleus and is 1,836 times heavier than the electron. The neutron is also in the nucleus and is 1,839 times heavier than an electron. If one compares the size of these particles with that of an entire atom, it is clear that they are minute. Much of the atom is made up of space in which these particles are buzzing about at their extraordinary speeds. The nucleus of

Elementary Particles

IN our conception of the universe we reached the upper limit of our knowledge of form. This is again the case at the lower end of the scale, where we have achieved so small a size that shape is unknown. We may, with the progress of science, push back these frontiers, but this is where we are at the moment.

the atom is far more dense, as we have already indicated, and therefore the space about the particles within the nucleus is less extensive, and the particles themselves relatively heavy. An atom has a diameter of roughly 10^{-8} centimeter and its nucleus will be about 10^{-12} centimeter. If looked at this way, it is clear that the nucleus occupies an absurdly small portion of the area of an atom.

One of the grand problems of modern physics is the structure of the nucleus. This is occupying the thoughts and energies of both the experimental and the theoretical physicist. They have made extraordinary progress in the last thirty years, but there still remain some of the most fundamental questions of how the atomic nucleus is organized. In this field, more than any other, all the work must be done by indirect evidence. This is not only because of Heisenberg's indeterminancy principle, but also because of the almost unbelievable smallness of the particles. The result has been a dual approach: one involving vast and powerful machinery, that is, cyclotrons and other kinds of accelerators, and the other involving a theoretical, mathematical approach to the problem. Both have made significant advances, and physics departments today emphasize equally the theoretical and the experimental.

On the composition of the nucleus there are several models which are being considered at the moment. One is that the particles are in shells; another is that the nucleus is like a liquid drop. Some of the facts fit perfectly with one of the models, and other facts with the other model, yet it is hard to visualize their both being correct. The difficulty is that in all systems with mutual attraction, solar and atomic, there is a central anchor (either the sun or the nucleus of the atom) about which everything revolves. Within the nucleus there appears no dominant body, and everything must be described in terms of more or less equivalent bodies and their relations to one another. This is a wholly new kind of problem for which there is no precedent, and therefore the progress has been exciting and slow.

Besides protons, neutrons, and electrons, numerous other elementary particles have been discovered. All of them, with the exception of the three mentioned, are short-lived when free from the nucleus.

They disintegrate rapidly into other particles, or else disappear with the emission of protons. There are also antiparticles, a concept which is exceedingly difficult for the nonphysicist to grasp. It is not helped by the statement that, according to the equations, a particle moving backward in time is equivalent to an antiparticle moving forward in time. However, this statement could not provide a better example of the fact that the further we depart from the size level of living creatures, the more remote we are from our expectations through our experience.

One important aspect of the particles in the nuclei involves their energies. If the proportion of protons to neutrons is altered, the result is an emission of energy which is called radioactivity. If the protons and neutrons of two atoms are allowed to fuse so as to form a new element, then the amount of energy released may be prodigious. This is, of course, nuclear energy. Of interest here is the fact that the nuclear energies are so great and that they can be unleashed. Usually, nuclei are protected from penetrating each other by their positive electric charges, which create a strong force of mutual repulsion. The trick, therefore, is to prevent this repulsion, and one way, as we said much earlier in the book, is to heat the atoms to extremely high temperatures. In such plasmas the electrons wander from the nuclei, and the nuclei may join (in a series of steps), thereby releasing vast quantities of energy. It is precisely this kind of nuclear fire that is thought to exist in the sun, where hydrogen nuclei are combining to form helium nuclei. Again we have the paradox that the smallest of units have vast quantities of energy in them, and it is this energy which is used by gigantic objects, namely, the stars.

Conclusion

14

I F WE ARE TO LOOK AT ALL OF SCIENCE, IT IS HELP-
ful and satisfying to classify the objects of science in some sort of
system. The one employed here is to put the objects in a size scale.
This crude and obvious system has the advantage, already emphasized, of showing that some objects are of a size that can be directly
observed, and others are not. But it is far more important that there
are properties which are correlated with size. For this reason it turns
out that size is fundamental and a useful criterion for arranging
objects. And let us now examine some of these correlations.

There is an interesting relation between the size of an object and
its speed of movement. If we go from the largest objects to the smallest ones, we find that stars and planets rush about at tremendous
speeds (100,000 to 200,000 miles per hour) ; the fastest large organisms are slower (40 to 70 miles per hour) ; and small bacteria travel
at a very slow rate (about 5 centimeters per hour) .

The only objects that appear to be incapable of any movement are

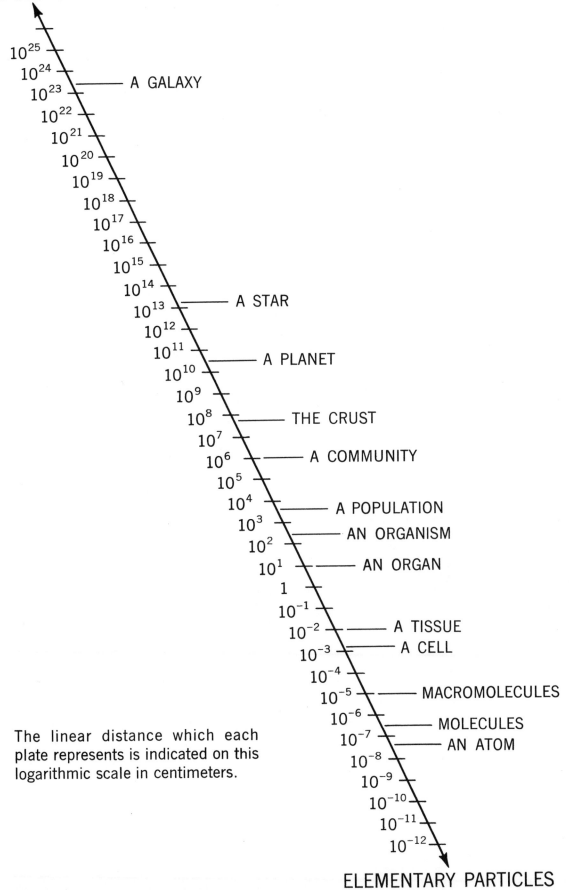

THE UNIVERSE

10^{25}
10^{24}
10^{23} — A GALAXY
10^{22}
10^{21}
10^{20}
10^{19}
10^{18}
10^{17}
10^{16}
10^{15}
10^{14}
10^{13} — A STAR
10^{12}
10^{11} — A PLANET
10^{10}
10^{9}
10^{8} — THE CRUST
10^{7}
10^{6} — A COMMUNITY
10^{5}
10^{4} — A POPULATION
10^{3} — AN ORGANISM
10^{2} — AN ORGAN
10^{1}
1
10^{-1}
10^{-2} — A TISSUE
10^{-3} — A CELL
10^{-4}
10^{-5} — MACROMOLECULES
10^{-6} — MOLECULES
10^{-7} — AN ATOM
10^{-8}
10^{-9}
10^{-10}
10^{-11}
10^{-12}

The linear distance which each plate represents is indicated on this logarithmic scale in centimeters.

ELEMENTARY PARTICLES

very large aggregates of molecules. Individual molecules begin to move about and, in fact, the smaller the molecule, the faster it moves. Therefore, at this lower end of the scale, the relation between size and speed is inverse, and the most minute objects, namely the elementary particles, are the fastest. They are even faster than the speed of stars and planets (they approach the speed of light, 186,300 miles per second).

In the case of stars and planets, it is not clear why these large bodies have such great speed. There is no reason to suspect any unknown or mysterious force; it is simply that we still need to know more of all of the activities of heavenly bodies. Space beyond our atmosphere has little matter in it, and therefore it is virtually devoid of causes for friction, so that if a body is moving, it will maintain a constant velocity over a long period of time. Its direction will be straight, or curved if it is affected by the gravitational force of neighboring bodies, but this gravitational force will not affect the velocity unless the bodies are brought into or near collision.

We have then a picture of all the gigantic structures in the sky moving at a relatively constant rate, or at least a rate which is changing very slowly over a long period of time, and therefore we narrow our question down to how they got their velocities in the first place. Initial velocities are the result of an expenditure of energy, and no doubt explosions of stars and other cataclysmic events have, in many instances, provided this necessary energy. In any case, all the bodies in the sky, down to the smallest planets (or even artificial satellites) move at a rapid pace and generally in fixed paths which may or may not be affected by gravity.

Let us jump now to the microscale of molecules and atoms. Here again the velocities of the molecules in a gas, or the electrons in an atom, are relatively constant. In the case of molecules, they do frequently collide, but instead of smashing or changing in any way, the molecules bounce apart and do so without loss of energy or speed (on the average). This is true even should they collide against the walls of a container.

This does not explain why the smaller the particle the faster it moves, a phenomenon which is as difficult to understand as the reverse relation for heavenly bodies. However, in the case of the movement of larger particles such as macromolecules, there is a clear explanation as to why they move slowly. From kinetic theory it can be shown that at a constant temperature the velocity of a particle is inversely proportionate to the square root of its mass. This relation is clearly illustrated in the case of Brownian motion.

If we look specifically at the elementary particles within the atom, there is a new feature. Besides the initial velocity, the direction of the paths may be affected by mutual forces (gravitational forces for stars and planets, and electrical forces for molecules). But the particles in the nucleus are held together by exceedingly strong forces qualitatively different from the forces of electricity or gravitation, and this gives atomic nuclei a remarkable stability of their own. As we have already emphasized, if a planetary system is disturbed it changes forever, but if an atom is disturbed it recovers. The only kind of disturbance that can permanently alter the nucleus of an atom is one which matches its tremendously high energy; hence the size and power of atom smashers.

The intermediate-size zone spreads from within a planet down to aggregations of large molecules. While the whole earth moves and rotates, the rocks within it are motionless with respect to one another. This, of course, is not quite true, for there are all sorts of crustal movements, but these are very slow, taking millions of years to travel any great distance, except for some localized sudden changes such as earthquakes and volcanic eruptions. Water flows on the earth's surface, and wind blows, both of which are largely mediated by the changing temperature related to the movement of the earth. Even gravity has its effect in the form of tides.

But of all intermediate-size objects, the most remarkable as far as motion is concerned are living organisms. Not only can large quadrupeds run some 40 to 70 miles per hour, but large birds can fly as fast and large fish can swim as fast. Furthermore, and even more remarkable, they can perform these feats at will, and they are not at the mercy of external forces. Running, flying, and swimming are all part of the process of food seeking, predator escaping, migration, and other aspects of animal existence. This is such a radically different kind of motion that we should examine it fully.

Consider it from an evolutionary point of view. Aggregates of macromolecules cannot move unless they are sufficiently small to be buffeted by the movement of small molecules. In order for a mass of substance the size of a bacterium to move, it has to build both a propeller and a machine to push the propeller. An energy-converting machine is necessary—a machine that can take chemical energy and convert it to mechanical energy, as occurs in muscle contraction. In fact, every activity of life requires such a machine, and the great step that occurred in the primeval ooze was the building of small metabolism machines called cells which could do things that their chemical components in disarray could not do. The organization of the cell machines therefore means not only motion but all the other opportunities which we associate with the notion of life. The fact that they can move is just one reflection of this more fundamental fact.

The appearance of energy machines in early earth history has many important aspects. The first is that the machines, in order to remain, must have some means of perpetuating themselves. The initial one could have remained fixed, like a rock, but that would mean no improvement, no progress. Therefore one of the essential uses of energy is a means of reproduction, or duplication, so that more machines like itself are produced. It is necessary, furthermore, that in this reproduction there should be a system of fixed inheritance so that one generation can be like its predecessor, but this system of inheritance must allow for fixed alterations (mutations) to occur that will be passed to the descendants. The latter conditions do not require energy, they are merely necessary conditions of the reproductive process.

By necessary conditions we mean that without them natural selection and therefore evolution would be impossible. In order for selection to occur, it is necessary to have reproduction and fixed inheritance (with variation), and in order to have reproduction it is necessary to have an energy machine. Just as atomic stability lies at

162

the foundation of the structure of matter, so these basic notions lie at the foundation of the nature of life.

Minute energy machines have properties which make them different from any other kind of physical system. In order for cells to metabolize, they require an incredible number of different parts. Since they are so small, the number of any one kind of part must be limited. They are, as we have already stressed, unique in their inhomogeneity. While it is true that the size difference between molecules and cells is so great that many molecules can fit into one cell, nevertheless there is nothing in the nonliving world to match the molecular variety and complexity of protoplasm. This inhomogeneity is a unique property of life.

Given energy machines, reproduction (with inheritance and variation mechanisms), and natural selection, all the diversity we find among animals and plants is possible. Increase in size and increase in speed have, with increase in the complexity of the biological environment, become for some organisms selectively advantageous and therefore they have prospered during the course of evolutionary time. These changes have resulted in other changes, some of which are dictated by new opportunities and some dictated by mechanical or engineering considerations. We find large organisms made up of many cells or many energy machines working in harmony. We find that even as size increases there is always one stage in the life cycle which is unicellular, a reminder of the fact that the inheritance mechanism of our ultimate ancestors was built to fit into one cell, and all life is founded upon that initial principle.

Energy machines have been constructed at only one size level in the universe. The reason for this may not be chance but the fitness of that size level. The requirements are that there be relatively little extraneous motion, so that the parts can come together, and furthermore the constituents must be diverse and have complex relations with one another so that a small machine is possible. This says nothing of how this fantastic feat was accomplished in the origin of life; we are merely arguing backward from what we know to exist.

Cells are just beyond the reach of any violent Brownian motion. It is also significant that life occurs only in a restricted temperature range, not too high, to prevent excess motion, and not too low, to prevent rigidity and stoppage of the machine. Molecules are minute by comparison to small cells, and therefore a small cell can contain a large number of molecules. The fact that atoms, which are limited in number, can combine to form great numbers of different kinds of molecules means that the cell, because of its size, has the ideal raw materials to make an energy machine. There is safety as well as danger in such a backward type of argument; the safety lies in the fact that this is precisely what has happened at this unique size level.

Science is about things large and small, and each size level brings its special characteristics and its special problems. It is even possible that we may at some future time extend the upper limit to beyond the universe and the lower limit to below the elementary particle. Whether this turns out to be true or not, we will always have enough problems, even at the most accessible of size levels, to keep us forever busy and happy in our search.

Index

Algae, movement of, 123
Alpha Centauri, 39
Amino acid molecule, illustration, 138–139
Amino acids, 130–131, 134
Amoeboid movement, 122-123
Animals:
    behavior, 74–77
        parent and offspring, 75
        pecking order, 76
        territory formation, 77–78
    brain, 101–103
    in community, 58–62
    diversity of species, 58, **63–64**
    food chain, 59–60
    geographical distribution, 58
    language, 76–77
    mating reactions, 75–76
    movement, 91
        size related to speed, 91, 124
    nervous system, 92, 96–101
    organs, 96–98
        sense, 97–100
    physiology, 90–92
    populations, 74–79
    prey and predators, 60
    respiration, 55
Aristotle, 23, 87
Astronomy:
    Big Bang hypothesis, 41
    early theories, 40
    modern techniques, 39–40
Atmosphere, 55
Atomic number, 146

Atomic physics, 147, 150–152
Atoms, 146–152; illustration, 148–149
    electrons in, 143, 146, 147, 150–151
    elementary particles in, 153–157; illustration, 154–155
    energy of, 150, 157
    in molecules, 143
    nucleus, 147, 150, 153, 156–157
    periodic law, 146–147
    periodic table, 146
    structure, 143, 147, 150
Auxin, 108

Bacteria:
    cell division in, 84, 85
    cells, 120
    chromosomes, 132
    enzyme synthesis in, 133
    macromolecules in, 137
    movement, 91, 123, 124, 158
    in rocks, fossilized, 54
    size and growth, 80–81
Balance of nature, 59
Bats, echo location, 98
Beadle, G. H., 134
Benzene ring, 145
Big Bang hypothesis, 41
Biochemical genetics, 134–135
Biochemistry, 111–115, 121–122
Biotin, 134
Birds:
    on Galapagos Islands, 73–74
    language, 76–77
    pecking order, 76

165

Brahe, Tycho, 40
Brain, 101–103
  hormones affecting, 115
Brownian movement, 140–141, 161

Cambium, 105
Cancer, 87
Carbohydrate polymers, 130
Carbon compounds, 143–145
  synthesis of, 144
Carbon cycles in community, 59
Carbon dioxide:
  in atmosphere, 55
  in photosynthesis, 55, 59
Cells, 117–126; illustration, 118–119
  complexity, 163
  cytoplasm, 86, 88, 121
  discoveries of Schleiden and Schwann,
      24, 117
  division, 84, 87–88
  movement, 122–124
  nucleus, 86–88, 117, 120–121
  permeability, 125–126
  plant tissue, 104–105, 121
  proteins in, see Proteins
  reproductive, 89
  sex, see Gametes
  single, as basis of growth, 84–85
  size, 120
  unicellular and multicellular organisms,
      84–85, 120
Cellulose, 130
Centrifuge, high-speed, 130, 132
Centrioles, 121
Chemicals:
  cycles of, in community, 59
  in rocks, 52
Chemistry, organic, 143–145
Chemoreceptors, 125
Chitin, 130
Chromosomes, 67, 70, 84–85
  of bacteria, 132
  crossing over, 70
Cilia, movement of, 122–123
Collagen, 132
Communication systems, electronic, 114

Community, 55–65; illustration, 56–57
  changes in, 62–63
  definition of, 58
  energy flow in, 59
  food chains in, 59–60
  niches in, 61, 64
Conditioned reflex, 100–101
Continental drift, 53
Copernicus, astronomical theories, 19, 24,
      40, 41
Coral islands, 53
Crick, F. H. C., 131
Crystallography, 49
Crystals:
  in minerals, 49, 52
  molecules in, 141–142
  structure, 142
  X-ray diffraction patterns, 142
Cytoplasm, 86, 88, 121

Darwin, Charles, 53
  fails to discover law of heredity, 66
  on Galapagos Islands, 73
  theory of natural selection, 19, 25, 58, 63
Democritus, 23
Deoxyribonucleic acid (DNA), 134
Diastrophic movements of earth's crust,
      53, 54
Diatoms, movement of, 123
Differentiation, 86–88
Doppler effect, 40

Ear, 98
Earth:
  age of, 54
  as center of universe, 40, 41
  central core of, 46
  crust of, 48–54; illustration, 50–51
    coastlines, advancing or receding, 53–
      54
    continental drift, 53
    movements, 52–54
  mantle of, 46
  as planet, 38; illustrations, 34–37
Earthquakes, 46, 53
Echo location, 98
Ecology, 58

Ecology (*Continued*)
  niches, concept of, 61, 64
  scientific method in, 27
Einstein, Albert, 20, 141
  theory of relativity, 24, 41–42
Electron microscope, 121–122
Electrons:
  combining of, 143
  mass and speed, 153
  number of, in atom, 146, 147
  wavelike properties, 150–151
Elementary particles, 153–157; illustration,
    154–155
  speed of, 160
  stability of, 161
Elements:
  periodic table, 146
  properties predicted, 147
Elk, 60
  eye of, illustration, 94–95
  individual, illustration, 82–83
  population, 76; illustration, 68–69
Elsasser, W. M., 133
Embryo, tissue interaction in, 109–110
Emergent evolution, 26
Endocrine glands, 111
Energy:
  assimilation in food, 90–91
  of atoms, 150, 157
  conversion of, in cells, 121
  flow of, in community, 59
  nuclear, 157
Energy machines in organisms, 162–163
Enzymes, 132–134
Erosion, 54
Ethology, 75
Evolution:
  emergent, 26
  isolation of species and, 72–74
  mathematical approach in population
    genetics, 70–71
  mutation in, 70–71
  natural selection, 19, 25, 58, 63
  size related to, 29
  see also Species, origin of
Eye, 97–98, 116
  of elk, illustration, 94–95

Eye (*Continued*)
  retinal layer, illustration, 106–107
  rod cells, illustration, 118–119

Fabre, Henri, 99
Feedback control, 114
Fisher, R. A., 71
Fossils, 53, 54, 62
Freud, Sigmund, 19, 102

Galapagos Islands, birds on, 73–74
Galaxies, 31, 38; illustration, 32–33
  number of, 31
  rate of movement, 40
  red shift in spectrum, 40
  size of, 31, 32, 38, 40
Galileo, 41
Gametes, 67, 70, 84–85, 89
Gases:
  inert, 147
  kinetic theory of, 24, 140
Gastrulation, 86
Generation time, 81
Genes, 84–86, 121
  dominant and recessive, 67
  functions of, 135
  Mendel's law of, 67
    exception to, 70
  nucleic acids in, 134
Genetics, 70
  macromolecules in, 134–135
  population, 71–72
  see also Heredity
Geology, 48–49, 53
Geophysics, 46
Gestalt, 26
Glaciers, 54
Gravitation:
  in formation of universe, 43
  Newton's law of, 43
Growth, 86–87
  of plants, 89–90
  size related to, 80–81
Growth hormone, 112

Haldane, J. B. S., 71
Haüy, R. J., Abbé, 142
Heisenberg, Werner, uncertainty princi-
  ple, 151, 156

Helium:
    in stars, 44
    in sun, 157
Heredity:
    cell as unit of, 120
    crossing over, phenomenon of, 70
    Mendel's laws of, 19, 24–25, 66–67
        exception to, 70
Hexadiyene, 145
Holism, 26
Hormones, 110–112
    growth, 112
    molecular aspect, 111-112
    plant, 88, 105, 108
Hydrogen atoms, illustration, 148–149
    in formation of stars, 43–44
    in space, 39, 43
    in sun, 157
Hydrogen bomb, 44
Hydrogen cycles in community, 59

Inheritance, *see* Heredity
Insects:
    behavior of, 78–79
    senses of, 99
Insulin, 111–112, 131
Islands:
    coral, 53
    volcanic, 53
Isolation of species:
    geographical, 72–74
    spatial, 72

Jastrow, Robert, quoted, 39
Jung, Carl Gustav, 102, 103
Jupiter, planet, 38; illustration, 34–35

Kepler, Johannes, 24, 40
Kinetic theory of gases, 24, 140
Koehler, Wolfgang, 26

Lashley, Karl, 101
Latex, 127
Learning, 101
Light, speed of, 30
Light-years, 30–31, 38
Limestone, 52
Linné, Carl von (Linnaeus), 23

Locomotion, 91, 161–162
    molecular movement compared with, 141, 162

Macromolecules, 127–137; illustration, 128–129
    in genetics, 134–135
    molecules and, 137
    passage into cells, 126
    in virology, 136
Marble, 52
Memory, 102
Mendel, Gregor, laws of heredity, 19, 24–25, 66–67
    exception to, 70
Mental disorders, biochemistry of, 112
Mercury, planet, 38; illustration, 34–35
Mesenchyme, 109–110
Metabolism, cell as unit of, 120
Microscope:
    electron, 121–122
    polarizing, 122–123
Milky Way, 31; illustration, 32–33
Mineralogy, 49, 52
Mitochondria, 121
Mitosis, 87, 117
Molecular biology, 135
Molecular weights:
    of molecules and macromolecules, 137
    of proteins, 130
Molecules, 137–145; illustration, 138–139
    atoms in, 143
    chemistry of, 143–145
    chemoreceptors and, 125–126
    in crystals, 141–142
    in earth's crust, 49
    in living and nonliving systems, 133
    macromolecules and, 137
    movement, 140–143, 160–162
        in kinetic theory of gases, 24, 140
    scientific method based on study of, 25–26
Moon, 38; illustration, 36–37
    tides caused by, 45
Morphogenetic movement, 86–88
Movement:
    of animals, 91, 161–162
    of cells, 122–124

Movement (*Continued*)
   of molecules, 24, 140–143, 160–162
   morphogenetic, 86–88
   of plants, 90, 93, 96
   speed of, *see* Speed
Muscular contraction, 100, 122
Mutations, 70–71

Natural selection, 19, 25, 58, 63
   mutations and, 70–71
Nature:
   balance of, 59
   scale of, illustration, 159
Neoprene, 127
Nervous system, 92, 96–101
   impulses, transmission of, 124–125
   motor nerves, 100–101
   sensory nerves, 96–100
   tissue of, 113–115
Neurons, 113–114, 124–125
Neurophysiology, molecular aspects, 112–
      113
Neurospora, 134
Neutrons, 153, 157
Newton, Sir Isaac:
   law of gravitation, 43
   laws of motion, 24, 41–42
Niches, ecological, 61, 64
Nitrogen cycles in community, 59
Nuclear energy, 157
Nuclear reactions in evolution of stars, 44
Nucleic acids, 130, 131
   in genes, 134
   in viruses, 136
Nucleus of atom, 147, 150, 153, 156–157
Nucleus of cell, 86, 117, 120–121
   division of, 87–88
Nylon, 127

Oceans, study of, 49
Organicism, 26
Organism, 80–92; illustration, 82–83
   cell as basis of, 84–85
   energy machine of, 162–163
   growth and development, 86–89
   life cycle, 85–86
   locomotion, 91, 161–162
   scientific method in study of, 26

Organism (*Continued*)
   size, 80–81, 84, 89
      speed of movement related to, 91, 124
Organs, 93–103; illustration, 94–95
   of animals, 96–98
      sense, 97–100
   of plants, 93, 96
Orlon, 127
Oxygen:
   in atmosphere, 55
   cycles of, in community, 59

Pain receptors, 100
Paleontology, 62–63
Parenchyma, 105
Pavlov, Ivan Petrovich, 100
Pecking order, 76
Periodic table of elements, 146
Phenylketonuria, 112
Phenylpyruvic acid, 112
Phloem, 104
Phospholipids, 126
Photon, 153
Photosynthesis, 55, 59
   movement and, 93, 96
Physiology:
   animal, 90–92
   plant, 89–90
Pinocytosis, 126
Pituitary gland, 111
Planets, 38; illustrations, 34–37
   chemical composition, 45–46
   origin, 44–45
   speed of movement, 158, 160
   study of, 46
   tides affected by, 45
Plants:
   anatomy and physiology, 89–90
   cells, 104–105, 121
   in community, 58–62
   diversity of species, 58, 63
   geographical distribution, 58
   growth, 89–90
   hormones, 88, 105, 108
   movement, 90, 93, 96
   organs, 93, 96
   photosynthesis, 55, 59
   populations, 74
   tissues, 104–105, 108–109

Plastids, 121
Pluto, planet, 38; illustration, 34–35
Polarizing microscope, 122, 123
Polar movement, 88
  in plants, 108
  in tissue of nervous system, 113
Polymers, 127, 130
  synthetic substances made from, 127
Population, 66–79; illustration, 68–69
  animal, 74–79
  human, 78
  isolation of, 72–74
Population genetics, 71–72
Porphyrins, 130
Potassium ions in nerve impulses, 124–125
Pressure, sensitivity to, 99–100
Proteins:
  amino acids in, 130–131, 134
  in cells, 123, 126, 130, 132
  functions, 132
  structure, 130
  in viruses, 136
Protons, 146, 153, 157
Protoplasm, complexity of, 163
Protoplasmic streaming, 122
Protozoa, 120
Pseudopods, 123
Psychology, 101–103
  gestalt, 26
Ptolemy, astronomer, 40
Purines, 131
Pyrimidines, 131

Quantum mechanics, 151
Quantum statistics, 27, 151

Radar, 98
Radioactive isotopes, 54
Radioactivity, 157
Red shift in galaxies, 40
Reductionism, 25–26
Relativity, Einstein's theory of, 24, 41–42
Ribonucleic acid (RNA), 112, 134
Ribosomes, 134
Rocks, 49, 52
  chemicals in, 52
  igneous, 49, 52

Rocks (Continued)
  metamorphic, 52
  sedimentary, 52

Scale of nature, illustration, 159
Schleiden, Matthias Jakob, 24, 117
Schroedinger, E., 150
Schwann, Theodor, 24, 117
Science:
  disciplines in, 29
  discoveries in, 18–20
  philosophy of, 21–22
Scientific method, 20–22
  description in, 22
  generalization in, 22–25
  molecules as basis of, 25–26
  organismal approach, 26–27
  reductionism, 25–27
  size of objects as basis of, 15, 18, 27–29, 41–42, 158; illustration, 159
Sense organs, 97–100
Sequoia, giant, 80–81
Sex cells, see Gametes
Sex hormones, 111, 115
Size:
  of objects, 15, 18, 27–29, 41–42, 158; illustration, 159
  of organism, 80–81, 84, 89
    movement and, 91, 124
  of prey and predators, 60
  speed related to, see Speed
  of universe, 30–31, 38–39
Smell, sense of, 99
Sodium ions in nerve impulses, 124–125
Space exploration, 45
Species:
  diversity of, 58, 63–64
  origin of: by isolation, 72–74
    by mutation, 70–71
    by natural selection, 19, 25, 58, 63
Speed, size of objects related to, 28, 40, 158, 160
  in molecule, 140–141, 160
  in organism, 91, 124
  in stars and planets, 158, 160
Spemann, Hans, 109
Spores, production of, 89
Stars, illustration, 34–35

Stars (*Continued*)
  evolution of, 43–44
  nuclear energy in, 157
  red giant, 44
  size of, 31
  speed of movement, 158, 160
  white dwarf, 44
Sugar molecule, illustration, 138–139
Sugars, polymerization of, 130
Sun, illustration, 34–35
  nuclear energy in, 157
  size of, 31
Svedberg, Theodor, 130

Taste, sense of, 99
Tatum, E. L., 134
Telescopes, 39–40
Temperature, animal and plant life related to, 58, 164
Temperature receptors, 100
Tides, 45
Tissues, 104–116; illustration, 106–107

Tissues (*Continued*)
  interaction, 109–110
  plant, 104–105, 108–109

Universe, 30–47; illustrations, 16–17, 32–37
  expansion of, Big Bang hypothesis, 41
  origin of, theories, 42–43
  size of, 30–31, 38–39

van der Waals' forces, 142
Viruses, 136
Vitamins, 130
Volcanoes, 53

Wallace, Alfred Russel, 19, 58, 63
Water molecule, illustration, 138–139
Water vapor in atmosphere, 55
Watson, J. D., 131
Wright, Sewall, 71

X-ray diffraction in crystals, 142
Xylem, 104–105

ABOUT THE AUTHOR

Dr. John Tyler Bonner, Professor of Biology at Princeton University and chairman of the Biology Department since 1965, is a scholar-teacher whose investigations of the development of organisms have broadened scientists' understanding of the problems of growth and cell differentiation. Recipient of the Selman A. Waksman Award for his contributions in the field of microbiology, his work has been largely concerned with the so-called "lower forms," algae, fungi, various invertebrates and especially the curious cellular slime molds.

Professor Bonner was born in New York City in 1920. A graduate of Phillips Exeter Academy, he received his M.A. from Harvard University. He then spent nearly four years with the Army Air Force, and later was on the staff of the Medical Laboratory at Wright Field. He received his Ph.D. at Harvard in 1947, basing his doctoral thesis on his first pioneering studies of the life-cycle of amoebae. He began teaching at Princeton in 1947.

In 1953 Professor Bonner held a Rockefeller Foundation Traveling Fellowship that enabled him to devote some months of study in the Paris laboratories of the eminent French biologist, Dr. E. Faure-Fremiet. In the spring of 1957 he was invited to give a series of special lectures at University College, London, and in 1958 he received a Guggenheim Fellowship to work at University of Edinburgh. He received a National Science Foundation Senior Postdoctoral Fellowship in 1963 which he used to work on a book in Cambridge, England.

Professor Bonner is the son of novelist Paul Hyde Bonner. He lives in Princeton, with his wife and four children. Among his other books are *Morphogenesis, Cells and Societies, The Evolution of Development, The Cellular Slime Molds,* and *The Ideas of Biology.*

Format by Katharine Sitterly
Set in Linotype Baskerville
Composed by American Book–Stratford Press, Inc.
Printed by The Murray Printing Co.
Bound by American Book–Stratford Press, Inc.
HARPER & ROW, PUBLISHERS, INCORPORATED

69 70 71 72 73 8 7 6 5 4 3 2 1